P9-DEZ-903

Financial Literacy for Children

Three Little Piggy Banks

Written by Pamela George • Illustrated by Meredith Luce

DC Canada Education Publishing

Written by: Pamela George

Illustrated by: Meredith Luce

Editors: Leonard Judge, Stephen Sedgwick-Williams

Copy Editor: S. Evelyn Cimesa

Cover Design: Meredith Luce

Published in 2016 by: DC Canada Education Publishing

180 Metcalfe Street, Suite 204
Ottawa, ON Canada K2P 1P5
www.dc-canada.ca

• •

Text © 2016 Pamela George
Illustrations © 2016 DC Canada Education Publishing

Printed in Canada

All rights reserved. No part of this book may be reproduced
in any form or by any electronic or mechanical
means including information storage and retrieval systems
without written permission of the copyright owner.

We acknowledge the financial support of the Government of Canada
through the Canada Book Fund for our publishing activities.

Three Little Piggy Banks

ISBN: 978-1-77205-176-6

• •

Library and Archives Canada Cataloguing in Publication
George, Pamela, 1969-, author
Three Little Piggy Banks / written by Pamela George ; illustrated by Meredith Luce.
(Financial literacy for children)
Includes bibliographical references.
ISBN 978-1-77205-176-6 (paperback)

1. Money—Juvenile fiction. 2. Thriftiness—Juvenile fiction. 3. Sharing—Juvenile fiction. I. Luce, Meredith, 1988-,
illustrator II. Title. III. Series. IV. Series: Financial literacy for children

PS8613.E5675T57 2016   jC813'.6   C2016-906313-5

Foreword

Financial literacy can be described as having the knowledge, skills and confidence to make responsible financial decisions. How we manage our money and make informed financial decisions has a profound impact on our ability to successfully manage our affairs and reach our financial goals. Sadly the level of financial literacy in Canada has declined in recent times putting a growing number of Canadians at risk of experiencing financial problems and hardship.

In her book, *Three Little Piggy Banks,* Pamela George answers the question we hear from people young and old "why don't they teach this stuff in school?" and takes us on an entertaining and practical journey of helping younger children learn and master the basic money skills of saving, sharing and spending.

With easy access to credit today, many adults have forgotten or never learned the value of delayed gratification and the feeling you get from knowing that you saved up and paid for something with your money instead of borrowed money. The *Three Little Piggy Banks* is a resource that parents and teachers can embrace and share with their children and students and help them learn these important life skills.

Scott Hannah
President & CEO
Credit Counselling Society

Note to Parents and Teachers

Every day, I see how financial illiteracy causes homelessness, addictions, broken dreams, sickness, broken marriages and broken children. I see firsthand how this epidemic is passed on from generation to generation, perpetuating the cycle of excessive debt and living pay cheque to pay cheque. My objective for this book is to give children an opportunity to finally break that cycle and allow them to be free from the burden of financial worries and to enjoy the freedom of financial sustainability.

It is never too soon to start learning about money and how to manage it. Let's educate the children who will grow up to become responsible and successful adults who, in the absence of financial worries, will have the capacity to focus on their dreams and live their life at their full and true potential.

Let's learn from Ella and Andy. Let's all learn about:

- Goal setting and planned spending

- Giving back

- Delayed gratification

- Keeping track of our expenses

- Talking openly about money, thereby removing its taboo and stigma

- Separating savings from spending

- Living within our means

To help children practise these skills, you will need:

- To give your child 3 dollars every week. It could be less or more but whatever amount you use it should be consistent and it should be able to be divided equally into three parts (saving, sharing and spending)

- 3 piggy banks or 3 jars or 3 bowls with lids

- Stars or coloured pencils to draw stars

- The worksheet at the back of the book (feel free to copy as necessary)

Pamela George

Ella and Andy are twins. On Sunday, they're both turning five years old. They're very excited.

While walking home from school, they talk about their perfect birthday presents.

"I want a camera so I can take lots of pictures!" says Ella.

"Well I want a bicycle, so I can ride
a two-wheeler!" says Andy.

Soon it is Sunday.
Ella and Andy can't wait
to get their presents.
They sit with their eyes closed.

"Surprise!"
say their parents.

Each of them has three little piggy banks sitting on the table.

"Happy birthday," says Mom. "We hope you like your gifts!"

Ella and Andy are confused.

"What are these?" both ask at the same time.

"These are piggy banks," Mom says.

"But what about our bike and camera?" Ella asks.

"Sweethearts," Mom says. "When I was young like you, I never got gifts for my birthday. Here you have beautiful gifts. You should say thank you.

"Your dad and I spent a lot of time trying to find the perfect gifts for both of you," says Mom.

"We know you don't understand it yet, but these gifts are very important and they will help you to get what you want," Dad says.

"Why are they important?" ask Ella and Andy.

"These gifts are important because they will help you to learn about money," says Mom.

"People who don't know about money, and how to use it wisely, can end up sad, angry or sick and may not even be able to buy food.

"We don't want that to happen to you, so it's time you learn how to use your money wisely."

"But why did you give us each three piggy banks instead of one?" Andy asks.

"What a good question!" Mom says.

"But first we need to name our piggy banks.

Let's call them **Saving, Sharing** and **Spending**."

"From now on, every week, your dad and I will give you an allowance of three dollars each," Mom explains.

"When you get your allowance, you can use all of it to buy things that you want. Or you can do something that is much more fun."

11

Mom suggests that they use the three little piggy banks this way: One dollar goes in Saving, one dollar goes in Sharing, and one dollar goes in Spending.

"This way, you can learn an important skill—how to use your money wisely," Dad says.

"This skill will help you when you grow up and start earning your own money," says Dad.

"Really?" The twins are getting excited.

"Then let's start!"

"The best way to use your piggy banks is to have goals," says Mom.

"We know you want a bicycle," Dad tells Andy. "Your goal is to save five dollars. If you can save five dollars, we'll add some more and help you buy your bike."

"Ella, we know you want a camera," Mom says.

"Your goal is to save five dollars, too. If you can save five dollars, we'll help you buy one."

Andy and Ella aren't sure. If they save, it will take weeks until they can get their gifts. But, they look at each other and say, "Okay. We will give it a try."

"A fun way to remember why we are saving is to decorate our Saving piggy banks with pictures of what we're saving up for," explains Mom.

Andy and Ella decorate their piggy banks with stickers. Andy puts stickers of bikes on his, and Ella puts stickers of cameras on hers.

"When we are saving for a goal, it's important to keep track of how much we're saving," Mom explains.

"To do that, we will use a worksheet and stars. When we want to know how much money there is inside the piggy banks, we just need to count the number of stars."

"Here, let's do one together!" Mom says, "This is how you place stars on your worksheets."

Their goal is to have five stars each. Mom shows them how to do it.

"What about sharing?" Andy asks.

"Remember when you both donated toys last Christmas?" Dad says. "That's sharing. Now that you have your own money, you can use it to help others.

"I share some of my money with a family in another country so they can buy food and medicine. Mom shares her money to help other moms who are in need," Dad says.

"My friend Vin is sick a lot, could I share my money to help him?" Andy says.

"Mommy, you said some people can't buy food," Ella says. "Could I help them with my money?"

"You two are so sweet," Mom says with a smile.

Mom shows them how to use the Sharing piggy banks.

"You'll put money in your Sharing piggy bank every week. When you have five stars, you can share the money, or you can wait longer and give more money. How does that sound?" Mom asks.

"Okay," both Ella and Andy agree.

"When you put money in your Sharing piggy banks, we'll put a star on your worksheet like this," Mom says as she points to the star on the worksheet.

"But what if we want to buy something for ourselves?" Andy asks.

"That's what the Spending piggy bank is for," Dad replies.

"The money you place in your Spending piggy bank can be used to buy whatever you want."

"So if I put one dollar in my Spending piggy bank, can I buy candy that costs one dollar?" Ella asks.

"Sure!" Dad says.

"I know. I'll get the purple ones I like! They're only a dollar each!" exclaims Ella.

"But what if I want to buy stickers?" Andy asks. "They're two dollars."

"You'll have to wait two weeks then," Dad answers.

"Oh," Andy replies. He's sad that he can't get his stickers right away, but they look cool.

"I guess they're worth the wait."

"That's right," Mom says.

"We will do the same thing with our Spending piggy banks as we did with the other two," says Mom.

She then picks up a pencil and explains, "We will put a star on your worksheet every time you put a dollar in, but when you take out a dollar, we willl help you cross out a star with an **X**."

Andy and Ella aren't sure at first, but after five weeks,
they save up five dollars in their Saving piggy banks.
They go with Mom and Dad to the store, and have

a lot of fun choosing the best bike and camera they
can afford. They feel proud that they saved up their own
money and helped to buy their gifts.

Andy sees his friend Vin a lot more. Vin becomes healthier. Andy is happy his Sharing money is helping his friend.

Ella collects lots of money in her Sharing piggy bank. She goes with her mom to buy food. She loves dropping off the food at the food bank.

Ella and Andy are happy that they now know how to use their money.

They try to think of different things that they can save for, and more ways to share their money.

And, of course, they love spending money on treats and stickers.

"We can SAVE for the things we want," Ella says.

"We can SHARE to help our friends and others," says Andy.

"And we can SPEND our money on fun things," both exclaim.

What would you SAVE for?

Who would you SHARE with?

And what would you SPEND on?

Will you join us?

Three Little Piggy Banks Worksheet

(Write your name in the space below.)

. . . .

Piggy bank names	Draw or place stars to track your money.
SAVING My savings goal: _____	☆
SHARING My sharing goal: _____	☆
SPENDING My spending goal: _____	☆

P9-DEZ-991

From the Library of

Julia Christensen-Hughes

B266   © 1983 by Armand Eisen   All Rights Reserved

Employee Involvement and Total Quality Management

EDWARD E. LAWLER III
SUSAN ALBERS MOHRMAN
GERALD E. LEDFORD, JR.

Employee Involvement and Total Quality Management

PRACTICES AND

RESULTS IN

FORTUNE 1000 COMPANIES

 JOSSEY-BASS PUBLISHERS
San Francisco

Copyright © 1992 by Jossey-Bass Inc., Publishers, 350 Sansome Street, San Francisco, California 94104. Copyright under International, Pan American, and Universal Copyright Conventions. All rights reserved. No part of this book may be reproduced in any form—except for brief quotation (not to exceed 1,000 words) in a review or professional work—without permission in writing from the publishers.

For sales outside the United States contact Maxwell Macmillan International Publishing Group, 866 Third Avenue, New York, New York 10022

Printed on acid-free paper and manufactured in the United States of America

Library of Congress Cataloging-in-Publication Data

Lawler, Edward E.
    Employee involvement and total quality management : practices and results in Fortune 1000 companies / Edward E. Lawler III, Susan Albers Mohrman, Gerald E. Ledford, Jr. — 1st ed.
      p. cm. — (The Jossey-Bass management series)
    Includes bibliographical references.
    ISBN 1-55542-434-1
    1. Industrial management—United States—Employee participation.
2. Total quality management—United States. I. Mohrman, Susan Albers. II. Ledford, Gerald E. III. Title. IV. Series.
HD5660.U5L38 1992
658.5'62—dc20
                                                           92-2557
                                                           CIP

FIRST EDITION
PB Printing   10 9 8 7 6 5 4 3 2 1   *Code 9248*

The Jossey-Bass

Management Series

CONTENTS

TABLES AND FIGURES

PREFACE

Employee involvement (EI) is an increasingly popular topic in the management literature. Proponents argue that it can provide a competitive advantage for companies that adopt it, because it produces superior corporate organizational performance. Our interest in employee involvement dates back decades and includes a considerable amount of research, as well as consulting. Despite great interest in the topic and a great deal of research, little systematic information exists on why companies are adopting employee involvement, what types of practices they are adopting as part of their employee involvement programs, and how effective they think employee involvement is. *Employee Involvement and Total Quality Management* attempts to answer these questions. It represents the second phase of a long-term project aimed at documenting the adoption of employee involvement practices by Fortune 1000 corporations.

The first phase involved a 1987 survey that focused on which types of employee involvement practices were being adopted by Fortune 1000 corporations and on their views of the effectiveness of these practices (Lawler, Ledford, and Mohrman, 1989). *Employee Involvement and Total Quality Management* reports on a 1990 follow-up survey of the Fortune 1000. This is the first study to report changes over time in the adoption rate for employee involvement practices among large U.S. firms. The study provides a benchmark of the degree to which employee involvement practices are actually used by U.S. corporations, and it allows conclusions about the rate of increase or decrease in the use of employee involvement from 1987 to 1990. It also provides extensive data on who adopts employee involvement and on the types of results that EI practices produce. It presents both an interesting story of increased utilization of employee involvement and a report of the effectiveness of employee involvement. In short, the study provides the first systematic data on what is happening with respect to employee involvement trends in the United States.

The information we present should be of use to managers who are considering the adoption of employee involvement and to researchers who are in search of data on how management practices are changing in the United States. Managers who are interested in comparing their own employee involvement efforts should find the data particularly interesting. It allows them to benchmark their own efforts against those of the Fortune 1000.

In addition to looking at employee involvement, the study also focuses on total quality management (TQM). There is little question that the practices that are part of total quality management have become increasingly popular in the United States and that their adoption is likely to continue. There is a close tie between total quality management programs and employee involvement programs. In our study we look at the relationship between the two, as well as at the rate of adoption of total quality management practices. These results should be particularly interesting to managers and researchers who are interested in the separate and joint impact of total quality management practices and employee involvement practices. To the best of our knowledge, this is the first study to look systematically at the adoption of total quality management. It also goes beyond simply looking at the rate of adoption and asks what combination of total quality management and employee involvement programs has a particularly positive impact.

Because total quality management and employee involvement are such important issues and interest such a broad audience, we wrote this book with a minimum of jargon and have avoided complex statistical analyses. Our objective was to make this book readable by any manager interested in employee involvement and total quality management. This is not to say, however, that the book does not report numbers. It does report extensive data, because the data are basic to an understanding of what is happening in the Fortune 1000 companies. We have attempted to present the data in a manner that is readable and easy to interpret. Managers, students, union leaders, employees, and anyone else interested in employee involvement and total quality management should find the book readable, and it should provide them with valuable insights into what is happening in major companies.

Overview of the Contents. In Part One, we address the adoption rate of employee involvement practices. We begin by looking at reasons for the adoption of employee involvement and then report on the use of information-sharing practices, knowledge-increasing practices, reward systems practices, and power-sharing practices. In each case, a comparison between practices in 1987 and 1990 is made, and an analysis is made of the use of a wide range of such employee involvement practices as self-managing work teams and gainsharing plans. Part One concludes with a section on patterns in the use of information, knowledge, reward, and power practices. The section provides a good sense of which practices appear together in organizations and of how different organizations are facing the challenge of balancing practices that affect information, knowledge, rewards, and power.

Part Two looks at the overall structure of employee involvement programs in companies. It focuses first on how employee involvement programs are implemented and on what types of policies, practices, and support are provided for employee involvement programs. It then looks at the use of personnel policies that can facilitate employee involvement. Our interest in these practices and policies is based on the view that they set the context for a successful employee involvement program. The last section of Part Two looks at major facilitators and barriers in the implementation of employee involvement.

In Part Three, we focus on the results of employee involvement programs. We look first at the success of programs that focus primarily on reward systems. For example, we ask about the success of skill-based pay systems, gainsharing programs, and profit-sharing programs. The results are generally quite favorable. Next, we examine the success of power-sharing programs, such as quality circle programs, self-managing teams, and job enrichment. Again, the results are generally favorable. The last section of Part Three reports on overall evaluations of employee involvement activities in companies. Their impact on both internal operating effectiveness and financial performance is considered. Again, the results are quite favorable. Companies consistently report that employee involvement has helped improve their internal operations and their overall financial results.

Part Four focuses on what types of organizations adopt employee involvement. It compares large companies with small companies and service with manufacturing organizations. Consistent patterns emerge, showing that some types of organizations clearly are using employee involvement more than others are. Part Four also considers unionization and the adoption of employee involvement. Finally, this part of the book focuses on the impact of the competitive marketplace that organizations face, as well as on its impact on the adoption of employee involvement practices. A clear relationship emerges, indicating that employee involvement is usually a direct response to market pressures, particularly those that involve global competition.

Part Five addresses the utilization of total quality management programs. First, the focus is on what practices are adopted as part of programs. Next, what type of company adopts total quality management practices is considered. There follows a consideration of the relationship between employee involvement and total quality. This analysis is particularly interesting because it focuses on the degree to which the two programs are adopted together and on how they are related to each other. Finally, the impact of total quality management programs is assessed. The focus here is not only on total quality programs but also on how the combination of total quality programs and employee involvement programs affects organizational improvement efforts.

Part Six explores the future of employee involvement. First, it considers the plans of organizations for adopting employee involvement practices, as well as their expected spending rate. Next, it looks at the types of changes that have occurred so far in the way the Fortune 1000 have been managed, and it considers what the next changes are likely to be.

Acknowledgments. Our study is part of the research program of the Center for Effective Organizations. The center, which is part of the Graduate School of Business Administration at the University of Southern California, is sponsored by a number of corporations interested in supporting research on management, and their financial support helped make this study possible. The Association for Quality and Participation provided partial funding for this particular study. We are grateful to the association and to our corporate sponsors.

A study like this one requires people in organizations to take the time to complete the questionnaires that we distribute. We are very appreciative of the time spent by members of the Fortune 1000 companies in responding to this survey.

Any research study of this magnitude also requires a high level of staff support. We are particularly fortunate at the Center for Effective Organizations to have a talented staff group that supports our research activity. We received excellent help in data collection and data analysis from Alice Yee Mark and Lei Chang. Kim Qualls provided help in the preparation of the manuscript.

Los Angeles, California   Edward E. Lawler III
March 1992   Susan Albers Mohrman
                                                    Gerald E. Ledford, Jr.

THE AUTHORS

Edward E. Lawler III is professor of management and organization in the Graduate School of Business Administration at the University of Southern California (USC). He joined USC in 1978 and in 1979 he founded and became director of the university's Center for Effective Organizations. Lawler received his B.A. degree (1960) from Brown University and his Ph.D. degree (1964) from the University of California, Berkeley, both in psychology. He has consulted with over one hundred organizations and four national governments on employee involvement, organizational change, and compensation. He has been honored as a top contributor to the fields of organizational development, organizational behavior, and compensation. The author of over two hundred articles and eighteen books, his works have been translated into seven languages. Lawler's most recent books include *The Ultimate Advantage: Creating the High-Involvement Organization* (1992), *Strategic Pay: Aligning Organizational Strategies and Pay Systems* (1990), *Designing Performance Appraisal Systems: Aligning Appraisal and Organizational Realities* (1989, with A. M. Mohrman, Jr. and S. M. Resnick-West), and *High-Involvement Management: Participative Strategies for Improving Organizational Performance* (1986).

Susan Albers Mohrman is senior research scientist at the Center for Effective Organizations, Graduate School of Business Administration, University of Southern California. She received her A.B. degree (1967) from Stanford University in psychology and her Ph.D. degree (1978) from

Northwestern University in organizational behavior. Mohrman has published papers and books on employee involvement, innovative approaches to the design of organizations, organizational development and change, high-technology organizations, union-management cooperative projects, and innovative research and evaluation methodologies. She was editor or coeditor of *Large-Scale Organizational Change* (1989, with others), *Managing Complexity in High-Technology Organizations* (1989), and *Doing Research That Is Useful for Theory and Practice* (1985, with others). Mohrman is coauthor of *Employee Involvement in America: A Study of Contemporary Practice* (1989, with E. E. Lawler III and G. E. Ledford, Jr.) and *Self-Designing Organizations: Learning How to Create High Performance* (1989).

Gerald E. Ledford, Jr. is senior research scientist at the Center for Effective Organizations, Graduate School of Business Administration, University of Southern California. He received his B.A. degree (1973) from George Washington University in psychology and his M.A. (1979) and Ph.D. (1984) degrees from the University of Michigan, also in psychology. He has conducted research, published, and consulted on a wide variety of approaches to improving organizational effectiveness and employee well-being, including employee involvement, innovative reward systems, organization design, job design, and union-management cooperation. Ledford has published over thirty articles and book chapters and is coauthor or coeditor of three books, including *Employee Involvement in America: A Study of Contemporary Practice* (1989, with E. E. Lawler III and S. A. Mohrman) and *Large-Scale Organizational Change* (1989, with others). He is co-winner of the Yoder-Heneman Personnel Research Award (1990) from the Society for Human Resource Management and was named an Ascendant Scholar (1991) by the Western Academy of Management.

Employee Involvement and
Total Quality Management

INTRODUCTION

Analyzing the Results of Employee Involvement

Employee involvement, participative management, democratic management, and quality of work life are familiar terms to most managers. They have been discussed by some and advocated by others for several decades now. The terms gained increased prominence in the 1980s because of the new economic realities that faced American business. To succeed, many American companies had to increase their performance significantly (Grayson and O'Dell, 1988; Dertouzos, Lester, and Solow, 1989). The most intriguing suggestion about how to improve performance was that American organizations change their organization and management systems to be more participative by involving employees in problem solving, decision making, and the financial success of the business. Finally, the time appeared to have arrived for widespread adoption of these not-so-new ideas.

In 1987 we did a study of the Fortune 1000 firms, in order to determine whether companies had incorporated employee involvement into their approaches to management (Lawler, Ledford, and Mohrman, 1989). Any assessment of corporate practices in the area of employee involvement needs to look at the prevalence of programs and practices that are consistent with it. The literature on employee involvement, however, stresses that it is more than just a particular program. It is an overall approach to managing. The involvement approach is based on the idea that organizations should be designed from top to bottom, so that employees are in control of their destiny and able to participate in the business of the organization.

In order to participate in the business, employees at all levels need power, information, knowledge, and rewards that are relevant to business performance. Among other questions, we asked about the degree to which business information, training and knowledge, power, and rewards (particularly rewards for performance) were spread throughout the organization. Of particular interest to us was the extent to which employees producing a product or offering a service had a sense of controlling their work, receiving information about their performance, and being rewarded for the performance of the organization.

True involvement takes more than just pushing any one, two, or three of the four key features—power, information, knowledge, and rewards— to all levels of the organization (Lawler, 1986, 1992). All four of these features must be moved to the lowest level of the organization. When this is done, and only when this is done, individuals performing the work can actually see a relationship between their efforts and the success or failure of the organization. Thus, in looking at the employee involvement practices of organizations, we studied the degree to which all four features were pushed downward.

With respect to the degree to which organizations were moving toward practicing employee involvement, the results of our 1987 study were mixed. For example, we asked how much quality circles, gainsharing plans, self-managing work teams, and other prime examples of employee involvement were being used. The results showed significant adoption rates for many practices that are associated with employee involvement. The results also showed that many key practices had only recently been adopted. Clearly, many organizations were trying to practice some form of employee involvement, but they often practiced it in only part of the organization, and in many cases they made only very limited changes. For example, they were more likely to use quality circles and other suggestion-type approaches than they were to use work-team approaches that made employees responsible for major decisions.

Companies generally reported that they were very satisfied with the results of their employee involvement activities and that they planned to expand them. These findings set the stage for the present study.

Purpose of the Study. This study examines the degree to which companies are using participative management practices, policies, and behaviors. It focuses especially on how much change occurred between 1987 and 1990. In addition, the study focuses on the reasons why employee involvement is being utilized and on the degree of compatibility between this approach and the environments that organizations face. It also investigates which organizational policies and practices are supportive of employee involvement, as well as the obstacles that prevent employee involvement from being implemented.

The present study does not stop with simply reporting on how companies are managed. It also focuses on the results that employee involvement efforts are producing for companies. Finally, it looks at how employee involvement efforts and total quality programs are related.

The study is intended to provide a good overview of which participative management practices and total quality practices are being adopted in the United States and of how adoption rates are changing. In addition, it identifies the kinds of organizations in which high-involvement practices are applicable and are being adopted.

Study Method. The data used in our 1987 study were gathered by the U.S. General Accounting Office (GAO). Michael Dulworth was the GAO project leader. At the inception of the study, the GAO brought together a consultants' panel to advise it on the study's design. This panel included experts on employee involvement systems from both the federal government and the private sector.

A design team, including the University of Southern California's (USC) Center for Effective Organizations (Lawler, Mohrman, and Ledford) and Michael Dulworth of GAO, developed the employee involvement survey questionnaire. The survey had three major sections:

1. *Company Practices/Culture:* This section asked questions about a corporation's information sharing, training, personnel policies and practices, and reward systems.

2. *Employee Involvement Innovations:* This section asked questions about the types of innovations adopted in order to increase employee involvement in decisions affecting work and the work environment.

3. *Employee Involvement Strategies:* This section asked general questions about the design and change strategy of a corporation's employee involvement efforts.

Our 1990 survey used many of the same questions that were asked in the 1987 survey. In addition, it asked a series of questions about total quality management programs and practices. These questions were added because of the increased interest in these programs and their potential impact on employee involvement. Resource A contains a copy of the 1990 questionnaire. A glossary defining the employee involvement terms accompanied both surveys. The glossary from the 1990 questionnaire is in Resource B.

Study Sample. The 1987 survey was sent by GAO to 934 of the companies listed in the 1986 Fortune 1000 listing of the 500 largest service companies and the 500 largest industrial firms. Because of acquisitions and mergers, the actual number of companies surveyed was fewer than 1,000. Responses numbered 476—about a 51 percent response rate. The responding organizations employ almost nine million full-time employees.

The 1990 survey was sent to 987 organizations on the 1990 Fortune 1000 list by the Center for Effective Organizations. Responses were received from 313 organizations, for a response rate of 32 percent. Ninety-two companies responded to both the 1987 survey and the 1990 survey.

Our 1990 survey used many of the same mailing and follow-up procedures that were used by the GAO in 1987 but did not obtain as high a response rate. The higher response rate to the 1987 survey was most likely due to its sponsorship by the GAO, a credible government agency. Nevertheless, a 32 percent response rate is impressive, given the large number of surveys being sent to companies today and the length of the survey (eighteen pages). It is a large enough return rate to allow us to make some interesting comparisons between the two surveys. It is also sufficiently large to allow us to make some interesting comparisons among the different types of companies that are represented in the 1990 sample.

A broad array of service and industrial firms is represented in the sample. Approximately half of both the 1987 and the 1990 samples come from the service sector, and approximately half come from the manufacturing sector. The median size of the organizations in both samples is between 9,000 and 10,000 employees. The median distribution of various types of employees in these organizations is almost identical, as the following tabulation indicates:

	1987	1990
Hourly/Clerical	59%	59%
Technical/Professional	20%	19%
Supervisory/Managerial	14%	14%
Other	7%	8%

Our conclusion is that the samples appear to be generally comparable, even though the response rate is somewhat lower for the 1990 survey. This is an important point, because it means that differences between the two surveys are likely to be due to actual changes in how the Fortune 1000 are managed, rather than being a product of different types of companies responding to the two surveys. Where possible, we checked this by comparing the 1987 and 1990 survey data for those companies that responded to both surveys. We generally found the results to be consistent with those found when the total sample was used.

In 55 percent of the cases, responses to the 1990 survey came from managers responsible for personnel or human resources. The other 45 percent were completed by a wide variety of senior executives, typically someone in the corporate office two levels below the chief executive officer (CEO).

Our data do have important limitations. Because they address only the 1,000 largest companies in the United States, they say nothing about what is happening in the vast numbers of smaller companies that constitute a large and growing part of the U.S. economy. Furthermore, they represent a view from the top. Senior managers completed the surveys. The views from other levels in the organization—from middle managers, front-line supervisors, and production workers—may be somewhat different.

Despite its limitations, this study is still the most comprehensive accounting of practices and approaches to employee involvement currently available. No comparable data set covers employee involvement activities in such a broad array of corporations. Particularly important is the possibility for comparing 1987 and 1990 data, in order to determine changing patterns of adoption and impact. This is a unique opportunity to investigate employee involvement efforts at various stages of implementation and in a variety of industrial and service organizations. We are confident that, from this study, we can produce research findings useful to all companies trying to engage the energies of their people more fully in addressing the competitive challenges that lie ahead.

PART ONE

*Adoption of
Employee Involvement
Practices*

SECTION 1

Reasons for Starting Involvement Efforts

Historically, there have been two major arguments made in support of the adoption of a participative management style. The first is that it will lead to more effective organizations (Lawler, 1986). The second is that it is a satisfying and ethically superior approach to managing (Sashkin, 1984).

Data from our 1987 study suggested that the vast majority of the firms that used employee involvement did so to improve the bottom line of the organization. As shown in Figure 1.1, this is still true in 1990. Companies are particularly interested in gains in productivity, quality, and employee motivation. Close behind is the desire to increase employee morale. Trailing far behind are value and ethical reasons.

In short, companies seem to feel that it is good business to practice employee involvement. This finding undoubtedly helps to explain why, even though the idea of employee involvement has been around for decades, it has received significant attention only in the last decade or two. Simply stated, in this period organizations have felt serious competitive pressures and have therefore been willing to consider management style changes.

Figure 1.2 provides data on the impetus for employee involvement. Organizations were asked who in the corporation provided the major stimulus for employee involvement activities. Given that adoption is usually for business reasons, it is not surprising that senior management seems to be the major stimulus for adoption. In over 40 percent of corporations, the chairman and senior executives were seen to be important stimuli for adoption. Employee involvement was less likely to be initiated by operation unit managers.

Unions are rarely seen as a stimulus, despite reports of increased interest on their part (Herrick, 1990). Moreover, employees are rarely seen as an important stimulus, although they are seen as a stimulus more frequently than unions are. Results for 1987 and 1990 are essentially the same. Most companies had begun their activities by the time of the first study (82 percent were active in 1987), so there is no reason to expect different results in 1990. The picture that develops is one in which senior

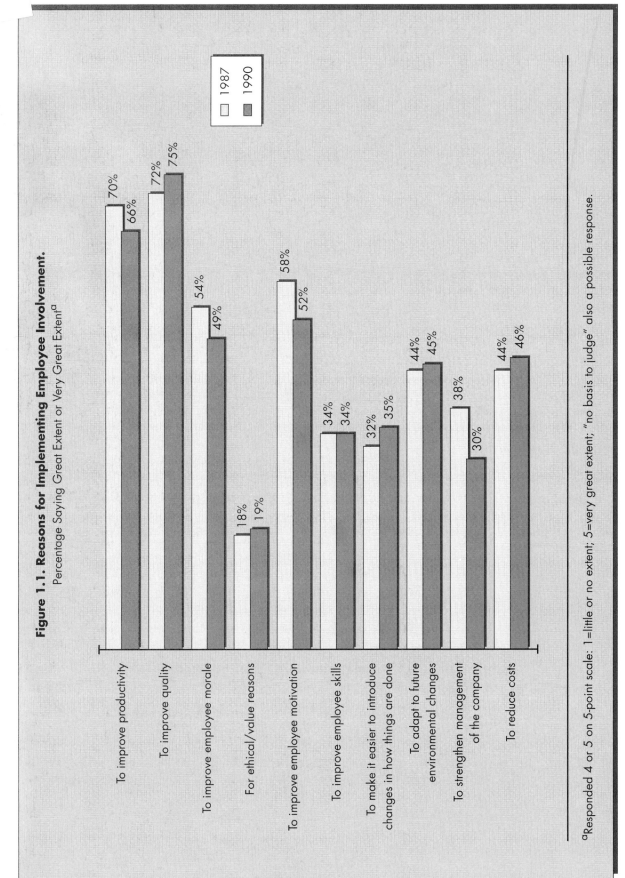

Figure 1.1. Reasons for Implementing Employee Involvement.
Percentage Saying Great Extent or Very Great Extent[a]

To improve productivity — 70% / 66%
To improve quality — 72% / 75%
To improve employee morale — 54% / 49%
For ethical/value reasons — 18% / 19%
To improve employee motivation — 58% / 52%
To improve employee skills — 34% / 34%
To make it easier to introduce changes in how things are done — 32% / 35%
To adapt to future environmental changes — 44% / 45%
To strengthen management of the company — 38% / 30%
To reduce costs — 44% / 46%

Legend: 1987 / 1990

[a]Responded 4 or 5 on 5-point scale: 1=little or no extent; 5=very great extent; "no basis to judge" also a possible response.

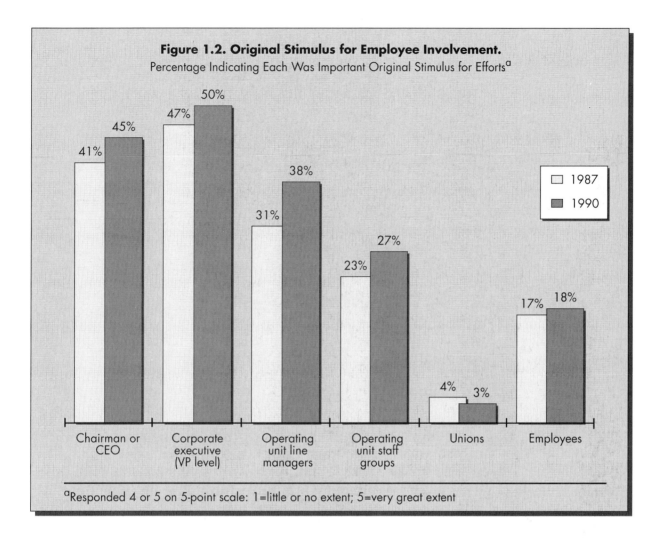

Figure 1.2. Original Stimulus for Employee Involvement.
Percentage Indicating Each Was Important Original Stimulus for Efforts[a]

- 1987
- 1990

50%
47%
45%
41%
38%
31%
27%
23%
18%
17%
4%
3%

Chairman or CEO | Corporate executive (VP level) | Operating unit line managers | Operating unit staff groups | Unions | Employees

[a]Responded 4 or 5 on 5-point scale: 1=little or no extent; 5=very great extent

management, operating unit management, employees, and finally (and to a very small extent) unions have provided the stimulus for organizations to install employee involvement.

SECTION 2

Sharing Information

Basic to employee involvement is the sharing of information about the business. Without business information, it is difficult for individuals to understand how the business is doing and to make meaningful contributions to the general direction of the business. Participation in planning and setting direction is impossible without information. In many cases, it is also impossible for employees to make good suggestions about how products and services can be improved and about how work processes in their areas can be carried out more effectively. Overall, in the absence of information, individuals are limited to simply performing prescribed tasks and filling roles in a relatively automatic way, and they are prevented from participating in the overall business direction and results.

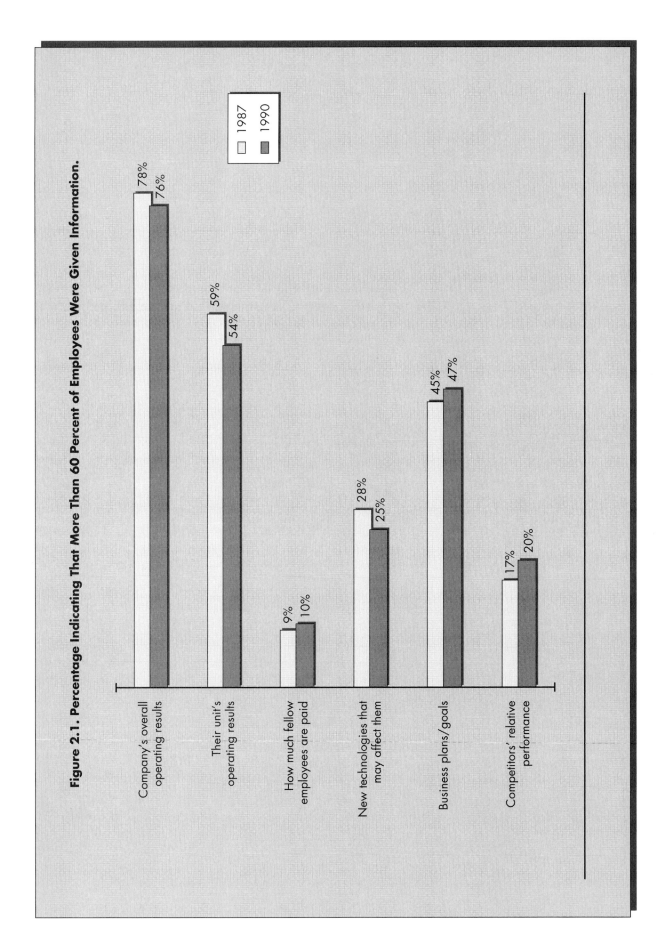

Figure 2.1. Percentage Indicating That More Than 60 Percent of Employees Were Given Information.

1987
1990

Company's overall operating results: 78%, 76%

Their unit's operating results: 59%, 54%

How much fellow employees are paid: 9%, 10%

New technologies that may affect them: 28%, 25%

Business plans/goals: 45%, 47%

Competitors' relative performance: 17%, 20%

Figure 2.1 illustrates responses to the question on the types of information that are shared. As this figure shows, most organizations share information about overall operating results with a high percentage of their employees. This was true in 1987, and it was still true in 1990. We anticipated this finding, since every organization in the study is a public corporation and, by law, must provide at least minimal information to shareholders.

If anything is surprising about the results shown in Figure 2.1, it is the number of organizations that do not share financial results with all employees, as well as the fact that this number does not appear to be increasing. Twenty-four percent of the companies still do not give most of their employees information about the company's performance, even though this is public information. The message here seems clearly to be that, in many companies, some employees are not treated as important stakeholders in and contributors to performance.

Although information about the overall performance of a large company is important in helping employees view the business as a whole, for practical purposes it may be of limited use to them. Corporate operating results are a considerable distance from many employees' job activities and may not be very directly related to what they do. Information on a unit's operating results is likely to be much more meaningful to employees. Therefore, this form of information sharing must be considered before any conclusion is reached about how companies perform with respect to information sharing.

As can be seen from Figure 2.1, 54 percent of the companies share data on the performance of work units with more than 60 percent of their employees. Therefore, nearly half of these companies do not regularly share unit operating results with most employees. Fewer than half (47 percent) of the companies provide regular information on the plans and goals of the business. In addition, it is clear from the data that the typical employee gets extremely limited feedback on relative business performance. Only 20 percent of the organizations provide data on competitors' performance to most or all employees.

As a general rule, the farther one gets from the results of the total corporation, the less likely it is that individuals are given business information. This is understandable, in one respect. Nothing requires an organization to distribute information about how the business is doing. Nevertheless, not distributing this information may entail significant costs and certainly is a major obstacle to employee involvement.

The typical employee in a company that does not share information may not understand how well the business is doing and is likely to have little sense of what the company must do to be competitive. Information about the performance levels of business units is often the most important information for employees to have if they are to be involved in a business for which they have a "line of sight." Awareness of corporate results is helpful in understanding the larger context, but the unit level is where most employees can make a difference and can relate to performance results. Information at this level is also what they need in order to contribute ideas and suggestions and be involved in the business.

The situation is similar with respect to information sharing about new technologies. Only 25 percent of the corporations say that they provide most of their employees with information about new technologies that may affect them. Without this information, it is impossible for employees to participate in the planning activities that are involved in the start-up of new technologies. Lack of information also prevents employees from preparing personally for technological transitions.

To get an idea of the concentration of these information-sharing approaches within companies, we counted the number of different kinds of information shared with at least 40 percent of employees. Table 2.1 illustrates the percentage of companies sharing from none to all of the six kinds of information listed in Figure 2.1. Again, the data from 1987 and 1990 are very similar. The 1990 data show that 41 percent of companies share four or more of the kinds of information with at least 40 percent of employees, but only 5 percent share all kinds. Not sharing salary information is understandable. Even though salary information is business-related, many individuals consider it to be a personal matter

Table 2.1. Information Shared with More Than 40 Percent of Employees.[a]

Number of Kinds of Information Shared	Percentage Saying Shared with More Than 40% of Employees	
	1987	1990
0	6	8
1	10	13
2	18	21
3	22	17
4	24	22
5	16	14
6	4	5

[a]Six possible kinds: company's overall operation results, unit operating results, fellow employees' pay, advance information on new technology, business plans/goals, competitors' relative performance.

(Lawler, 1990). The same is not true for the other types of data, however. Sharing all or most of these kinds of information may be a necessary precondition for high levels of employee involvement.

Do employee involvement programs increase the information flow in organizations? As shown in Figure 2.2, the answer appears to be yes. The most common response to this question in both 1987 and 1990 was that involvement activities increase information flow to a moderate degree. This is to be expected, since information is so critical to all aspects of involvement. If anything is surprising, it is that the responses to this question are not more positive.

Our results show that Fortune 1000 corporations share only limited information with employees. There is little sign of change from 1987 to 1990, despite acceptance of the idea that information sharing is a critical part of many involvement and total quality programs. In essence, many organizations provide only what the law requires them to make available to shareholders: overall business results. Most employees do not get good information on the direction and success of the business. Therefore, it is hard to imagine employees being meaningfully involved in decisions that affect anything more than their immediate job duties.

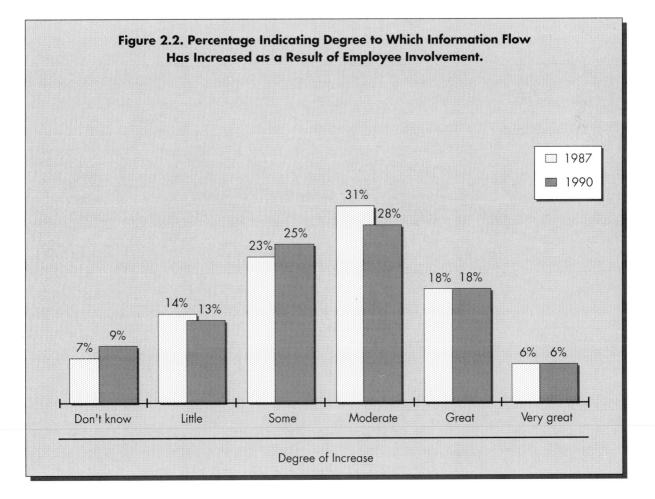

Figure 2.2. Percentage Indicating Degree to Which Information Flow Has Increased as a Result of Employee Involvement.

SECTION 3

Increasing Knowledge

Much of the writing on national competitiveness during the 1980s and early 1990s has stressed the importance of skill development (for example, see Reich, 1991; Porter, 1990). Similar conclusions have been reached by studies that have focused on the condition of schools in the United States (Secretary's Commission on Achieving Necessary Skills, 1991). This is hardly surprising; without the right skills, it is impossible for individuals to participate in the business and influence its direction. At a more basic level, it is impossible for individuals without skills to do most jobs effectively.

Table 3.1 reports on the prevalence of training for the types of skills frequently identified as being necessary for effective employee involvement (Commission on the Skills of the American Workforce, 1990). Three of these skills are essentially interpersonal and group skills. These are included because so many employee involvement processes involve meetings, interpersonal interactions, and influencing others. The two technical skills, quality/statistical analysis and business understanding, are included because they are central to the content of organizational improvement efforts and total quality management programs. Finally, we asked about job skills training (1990 only).

As can be seen from this table, most employees, in a three-year period, did not receive training in interpersonal skills or in the kinds of technical/analytical skills necessary for an employee involvement or total quality program to work effectively. These results are essentially no different from those that were obtained in 1987. Despite the widely heralded com-

Table 3.1. Percentage Indicating That More Than 60 Percent of Employees Had Training in Past Three Years.

Type of Training	1987	1990
Group decision-making/problem-solving skills	5	6
Leadership skills	4	3
Skills in understanding the business (accounting, finance, etc.)	4	2
Quality/statistical analysis skills	6	9
Team-building skills	5	8
Job skills training	N/A	35

mitment to total quality management and statistical analysis that is professed by many organizations today, only 9 percent of the organizations have recently trained more than 60 percent of their employees in these skills (Deming, 1986; Juran, 1989). Similarly, despite the importance of employees' understanding the business, only 2 percent of organizations have recently trained more than 60 percent of their employees in understanding financial reports and business results. Given this lack of training, it is unreasonable to expect employees to understand business performance and be able to contribute to it.

The situation is much the same with respect to interpersonal skills. Individuals simply are not trained in the interpersonal skills needed for them to participate in problem-solving groups and team-based decision making.

The data are somewhat more positive with respect to job skills; 35 percent of the companies surveyed provided training to most of their employees. Still, this stands in notable contrast to the policies of such exemplary companies as IBM and Motorola, which mandate one week's training for all employees each year (for example, see Wiggenhorn, 1990).

What accounts for the apparently poor record of most corporations in the area of training? One possibility is that we set the hurdle too high by asking about training only in the previous three years. It may be that many organizations trained their employees earlier. Unfortunately, there is no way of knowing whether this is true.

It may also be that 60 percent was too high a threshold for many companies to reach. Table 3.2 uses a lower threshold, 20 percent. This picture

Table 3.2. Percentage Indicating That More Than 20 Percent of Employees Had Training in Past Three Years.

Type of Training	1987	1990
Group decision-making/problem-solving skills	57	55
Leadership skills	63	54
Skills in understanding the business (accounting, finance, etc.)	50	39
Quality/statistical analysis skills	42	43
Team-building skills	52	56
Job skills training	N/A	84

is somewhat more encouraging. The 1990 data suggest that at least half the organizations are doing limited training in these areas; this is not very different from the 1987 picture. Particularly encouraging is the total of 84 percent for job training. Nevertheless, a note of caution is in order. This number may represent nothing more than a commitment to traditional on-the-job training.

A count of how many types of training are being done by each company is displayed in Table 3.3. This table shows that during the three years before these data were collected, only 1 percent of the responding companies trained 40 percent or more of their employees in all these areas. Fifty-nine percent did not train 40 percent or more in any of the areas. These figures show little change from 1987 to 1990. The results change significantly when job skills are included as a kind of training, as shown in Table 3.4. With job skills included, 34 percent of the companies provided no training in these areas to 40 percent or more of their employees.

Do employee involvement programs lead to more training and skill development? The data in Figure 3.1 suggest that the answer is yes. Most companies indicate that employee involvement has led to some increase or moderate increase in skill development. This tendency shows a slight increase over the 1987 data.

These data suggest a tremendous void in the training of American workers. Most major U.S. corporations apparently have not made the kind of investment in training that would be needed for successful employee involvement. This is particularly distressing, given the many studies

Table 3.3. Training Provided to More Than 40 Percent of Employees in Past Three Years.[a]

Number of Kinds of Training Provided	Percentage Saying More Than 40% of Employees Given	
	1987	1990
0	63	59
1	16	22
2	12	8
3	6	7
4	2	2
5	1	1

[a]Five possible kinds: decision making/problem solving, leadership, business understanding (accounting, etc.), quality/statistical analysis, team building.

Table 3.4. Training Provided to More Than 40 Percent of Employees in Past Three Years.[a]

Number of Kinds of Training Provided	Percentage Saying More Than 40% of Employees Given
	1990
0	34
1	32
2	19
3	6
4	6
5	2
6	1

[a]Six possible kinds: decision making/problem solving, leadership, business understanding (accounting, etc.), quality/statistical analysis, team building, job skills.

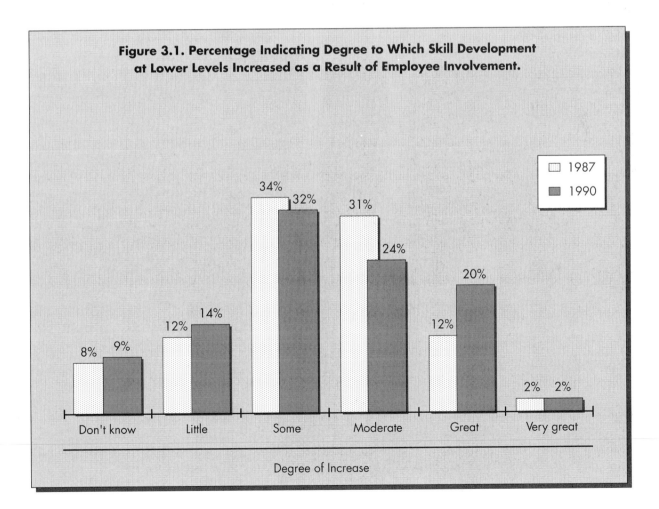

Figure 3.1. Percentage Indicating Degree to Which Skill Development at Lower Levels Increased as a Result of Employee Involvement.

1987
1990

Don't know — 8% / 9%
Little — 12% / 14%
Some — 34% / 32%
Moderate — 31% / 24%
Great — 12% / 20%
Very great — 2% / 2%

Degree of Increase

showing that the American work force is often poorly prepared in businesses that face global competition (Dertouzos, Lester, and Solow, 1989; Reich, 1991). For employee involvement to work—indeed, for most businesses to work, regardless of what management approaches they use—a substantially greater investment in human resource development is indicated at both the societal and the corporate levels.

SECTION 4

Rewarding Performance

Basing rewards on organizational performance is one way to ensure that employees are involved in and care about the performance of the organization (Lawler, 1990). It also helps ensure that they share in the gains that result from any performance improvement. Table 4.1 shows the popularity of five approaches to paying for performance.

Individual incentive plans are usually not particularly supportive of employee involvement. They focus on individuals and do not tie the individual into the overall success of the business; moreover, they can interfere with teamwork and problem solving. The pattern for individual incentives shown in Table 4.1 is interesting. All but 10 percent of the corporations report having some employees covered by individual incentives, but these systems usually cover less than 41 percent of the work force. A comparison between 1987 and 1990 shows no significant change in the use of individual incentive plans.

Table 4.1. Percentage of Employees Covered by Performance-Based Rewards.

		None 0%	Almost None 1–20%	Some 21–40%	About Half 41–60%	Most 61–80%	Almost All 81–99%	All 100%
Individual incentives	1987	13	49	27	6	2	1	2
	1990	10	46	24	8	5	3	4
Team incentives	1987	Not asked in 1987	—	—	—	—	—	
	1990	41	38	10	6	1	2	3
Profit sharing	1987	35	20	11	4	5	10	15
	1990	37	19	7	4	6	10	17
Gainsharing	1987	74	19	4	1	0	1	1
	1990	61	28	8	1	1	1	0
Stock ownership	1987	39	8	4	4	6	10	28
	1990	36	9	6	3	5	12	29

Team incentives can be supportive of employee involvement activities, such as work teams and problem-solving groups. They are used by 59 percent of all companies, although when used they tend to cover small numbers of employees (20 percent or less). This finding makes sense: many individuals do not work in teams, and so using team incentives for them is not appropriate.

Profit sharing, employee stock ownership, and gainsharing are approaches that link employees more closely to the success of the business and reward them for it. These systems are often cited as reward approaches supportive of employee involvement (Lawler, 1990; Blinder, 1990). Profit sharing and employee stock ownership are the most widely used and the most likely to be available to most or all employees.

Particularly interesting is the fact that stock ownership is available to all employees in 29 percent of the corporations surveyed. Although we did not collect data on the reasons, it is likely that this result reflects the widespread use of stock purchase plans (Blasi, 1988; Rosen, Klein, and Young, 1986). In 36 percent of the corporations surveyed, by contrast, stock ownership is not a plan available to any employees. It is one practice that companies tend to offer to all or none of their employees.

Only 17 percent of the companies cover *all* employees with profit sharing, and only 63 percent cover *any* of their employees with profit-sharing plans. Many profit-sharing plans defer payments until retirement (Lawler, 1990). Therefore, it seems safe to conclude that profit sharing is not acting as an important motivator of involvement or performance in most companies. A comparison between the 1987 results and the 1990 results shows no significant increase in the use of profit sharing, despite an increasing emphasis in the management literature on the use of variable or bonus-based pay (Blinder, 1990; Weitzman, 1984).

As shown in Table 4.1, gainsharing is clearly the least popular approach. Sixty-one percent of responding companies say none of their employees are covered by a gainsharing plan. Gainsharing is also the approach that historically has been most closely identified with employee involvement, since it stresses involvement as key to the success of the financial bonus system. Of the corporations that have some employees on gainsharing, virtually all have a minority of the total work force on it. Rare (only 1 percent of the companies that responded in 1987) is the corporation that covers all employees with gainsharing.

A comparison between the 1987 and 1990 results shows a significant increase in the use of gainsharing. Thirteen percent of the companies that responded started their first gainsharing plans in the last three years; others increased the number of employees covered by gainsharing plans. Apparently, gainsharing is the pay approach that many companies are increasingly adopting in order to increase the amount of variable pay they offer. Given the importance of pay to the cost structures of most businesses, as well as the usually slow rate of change in pay practices, this increased use of gainsharing in just a three-year period is particularly noteworthy.

The actual involvement-oriented reward activity may be a bit inflated in Table 4.1 because profit sharing and employee stock ownership plans (ESOPs) are included in the numbers. Many profit-sharing plans have been around for years, and such a plan often is best thought of as a fringe benefit rather than an incentive. Many ESOPs have been installed for tax advantages and are not tied to employee involvement (Blasi, 1988). In addition, the effectiveness of profit sharing plans and ESOPs can be questioned, for two reasons. First, the "line of sight" for profit sharing and ESOPs is often quite poor. Individual employees may not know how to affect such distant, aggregate measures as profit or stock price. Second, the general lack of information about the business that exists in many companies limits the line of sight even more. Without information and knowledge, rewards often appear arbitrary and capricious, rather than motivating and involving.

All-salaried pay systems and knowledge-/skill-based pay are both frequently considered to be supportive of employee involvement. All-salaried pay reduces the distinctions between classifications of employees, thus promoting a situation in which the pay system is congruent with the

Table 4.2. Percentage of Employees Covered by Reward Systems.

		None 0%	Almost None 1–20%	Some 21–40%	About Half 41–60%	Most 61–80%	Almost All 81–99%	All 100%
All-salaried pay	1987	29	15	13	10	12	11	10
	1990	36	18	14	10	7	9	7
Knowledge-/ skill-based pay	1987	60	25	7	2	2	2	2
	1990	49	34	11	2	1	1	1
Flexible benefits	1987	66	7	4	3	2	6	13
	1990	46	12	5	4	5	9	20
Nonmonetary	1987	Not asked in 1987		—	—	—	—	—
	1990	9	23	18	10	13	10	17

notion that information, knowledge, and power are shared. Table 4.2 shows that almost two-thirds of companies use this approach, to some extent. A comparison between 1987 and 1990 shows no increase in the use of all-salaried work forces. If anything, there is a slight decrease.

When pay is based on knowledge and skill, it rewards individuals for their capability and flexibility in contributing to the organization. As a person learns more and can contribute more to the organization, pay is increased (Ledford, 1991). This fosters and rewards cross-training and makes possible the flexible deployment of people. It can also be supportive of teaming and encouraging individuals to learn the skills they need to be involved in the business. Finally, it promotes a broader understanding of how the business operates, a skill that can be useful in addressing complex problems. Fifty-one percent of companies use this approach to some extent, although most with only a minority of the work force.

A comparison between the 1987 and the 1990 data shows a significant increase in the use of skill-based pay. The number of companies using it increased, from 40 percent to 51 percent. As was true with the increased use of gainsharing, this change is impressive. In some respects, it is a change more significant than the increased use of gainsharing. Skill-based pay is not an "extra." It represents a major change in the way an organization determines base pay. Many base-pay systems have been in place for decades and cannot be changed easily, particularly not in the major way that they must be changed if skill-based pay is adopted. Therefore, it is particularly impressive that, in the short period of three years, significant changes have occurred in the use of skill-based pay.

Flexible benefits programs provide employees with some control over how the benefit portion of the compensation package is distributed. This approach fits with the employee involvement philosophy of moving decision making to the lowest possible level. Fifty-four percent of companies use this approach.

Flexible benefits increased tremendously in popularity from 1987 to 1990. Twenty percent more companies reported having flexible benefits in 1990 than in 1987. In addition, seven percent more reported covering all their employees with flexible benefits. Although flexible benefits programs fit with employee involvement because of their emphasis on employee choice in the reward mix, the increased adoption of this approach may have more to do with controlling benefit costs and meeting the needs of an increasingly diverse work force than with supporting employee involvement. The cost of benefits has been increasing dramatically, and some companies are using flexible benefits and cost sharing as ways to control costs (Lawler, 1990).

Recognition programs are sometimes used to support employee involvement efforts. Table 4.2 shows that most organizations have recognition, or nonmonetary, programs, but in only 17 percent of the responding companies do they cover all employees. This figure suggests that they typically are targeted at special activities and groups and are not used to support broad involvement systems.

Table 4.3 shows the concentration of the five pay-for-performance reward system approaches. Twenty-nine percent of companies are using none of them widely, and only 10 percent use three or more widely. The results clearly establish that most organizations do not make significant efforts to reward most individuals for organizational performance. Given the current level of use, the opportunity exists for most organizations to reward many more individuals for organizational performance and to increase their level of involvement in the organization.

To get a better feel for how different reward system practices are combined, we compared companies that use skill-based pay with those that do not. The results show that the pay practices of companies that use skill-based pay are significantly different from those that do not. As can be seen in Table 4.4, companies that use it are much more likely to have all-salaried work forces and to use profit sharing, gainsharing, and team incentives. The strong association between the use of skill-based pay and the three approaches to pay for performance is interesting. Gainsharing in particular seems to fit well with skill-based pay. It is strongly associ-

Table 4.3. Rewards Used with More Than 40 Percent of Employees.[a]

Number of Kinds of Rewards Provided	Percentage Saying More Than 40% of Employees Have
	1990
0	29
1	38
2	24
3	8
4	2
5	0

[a]Five possible kinds: individual incentives, profit sharing, gainsharing, stock ownership, team incentives.

ated with employee involvement, but it addresses performance motivation, whereas skill-based pay is designed to encourage skill development (Lawler, 1990). In this respect, the two approaches complement each other, and so using them together makes sense. The same is true of profit sharing and team incentives, although they do not have a strong historical tie to employee involvement.

Figure 4.1 suggests that the responding companies feel employee involvement has had a limited effect on the degree to which performance-based rewards have increased at lower levels. In fact, accorcding to our respondents, rewards have been less affected by employee involvement than information sharing and knowledge have. The 1990 and 1987 data show similar results.

Overall, moving performance-based rewards throughout an organization and adding skill-based pay may be difficult but in all likelihood critical to the success of employee involvement. Failure to take these steps may limit the effectiveness of employee involvement efforts, since employees see themselves as having little direct stake in organizational performance and do not feel rewarded for adding to their skills. Although the overall rate of use of gainsharing and skill-based pay is relatively low, the increase in their use between 1987 and 1990 is significant.

Table 4.4. Pay Practices Related to Use of Skill-Based Pay.

Pay Practice	Percentage of Companies Without Skill-Based Pay Using	Percentage of Companies With Skill-Based Pay Using
All-salaried	53	75
Profit sharing	54	71
Gainsharing	19	59
Team incentives	49	68
Stock ownership	59	69
Individual incentives	86	92
Nonmonetary	88	94
Flexible benefits	51	58

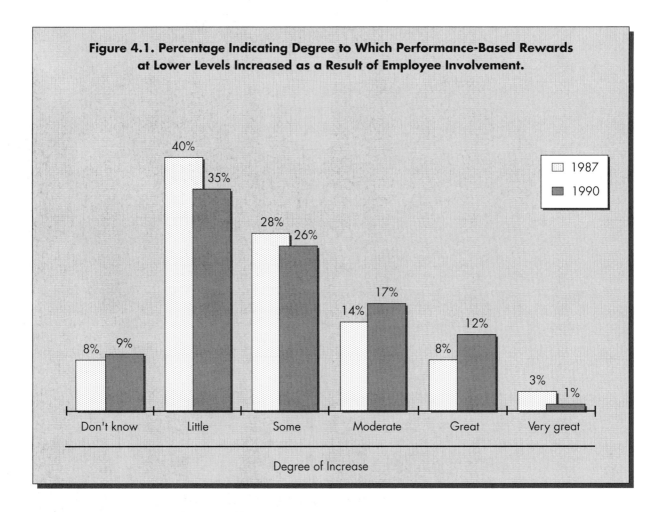

Figure 4.1. Percentage Indicating Degree to Which Performance-Based Rewards at Lower Levels Increased as a Result of Employee Involvement.

Legend: 1987, 1990

Don't know: 8%, 9%
Little: 40%, 35%
Some: 28%, 26%
Moderate: 14%, 17%
Great: 8%, 12%
Very great: 3%, 1%

Degree of Increase

SECTION 5

Redistributing Power

Moving power downward in organizations often requires special activities and structural changes. To get a sense of how active organizations are in moving decision making to lower levels, the survey asked about the existence of a number of specific approaches. These approaches can be divided into two basic types.

The first type involves special meetings or information-dissemination activities that are separate from the normal day-to-day work processes. These are often referred to as *parallel organizational structures* (Lawler and Mohrman, 1985; Lawler, 1988). The best-known activity is the use of quality circles. Although these do move some power downward, they are very limited in their impact (Ledford, Lawler, and Mohrman, 1988). Typically, employees only provide input and recommendations to decisions; they do not make substantial decisions (some parallel organizational structures do permit employees to make certain decisions).

As can be seen in Table 5.1, the majority of organizations report using some form of parallel structure. Quality circles are used in 66 percent of all companies. Other types of participation groups are used by 86 percent of all companies. The use of parallel structures is typically limited to much fewer than half the employees in an organization. This necessarily limits their impact, because organizations are sharing only a limited amount of power with a limited number of employees.

A comparison of the 1987 data with the 1990 data shows an increase in the use of problem-solving approaches. The increase in the use of non–quality circle approaches is particularly impressive, both because of the size of the increase (16 percent more companies used them in 1990) and because of the number of companies that were already using them.

Union-management quality of work life (QWL) committees have been tried in a much smaller percentage of the companies. This, of course, follows from the relatively low level of union membership in the United States and in these companies. A comparison between 1987 and 1990 shows a 10 percent increase in the percentage of companies using this approach. Like other parallel participation practices, this one is clearly growing in popularity.

Survey feedback does not necessarily entail the establishment of a parallel structure, since it often occurs in established work groups. It is often

Table 5.1. Power-Sharing Practices for Generating Employee Suggestions and Problem Solving.

Percentage of Employees Currently Involved

Innovation/ Program		None 0%	Almost None 1–20%	Some 21–40%	About Half 41–60%	Most 61–80%	Almost All 81–99%	All 100%
Quality circles	1987	39	32	18	7	2	0	1
	1990	34	36	19	7	4	1	1
Participation groups other than QCs	1987	30	33	21	9	3	2	1
	1990	14	35	30	11	5	3	3
Union-management QWL committee	1987	70	20	7	2	1	1	0
	1990	60	26	11	2	0	0	1
Survey feedback	1987	32	22	17	6	7	6	10
	1990	23	26	20	5	4	7	16

seen as an "extra" or a special activity, however. As seen in Table 5.1, 77 percent of companies use this for at least some employees. It too shows a significant increase in popularity from 1987 to 1990.

Table 5.2 shows that the situation is different when it comes to the three programs that are part of the second approach to moving power downward. Job enrichment, self-managing work teams, and minienterprise units involve a substantial change in the basic structure of the organization and are aimed at moving important decisions into the hands of the individuals and teams performing the basic manufacturing or service work of the company.

As shown in Table 5.2, job enrichment is used rather widely. The broad acceptance of job enrichment probably results from the fact that this approach has been around for several decades and was widely publicized in the 1970s (see Herzberg, 1966; Hackman and Oldham, 1980). Nevertheless, job enrichment programs typically affect fewer than 20 percent of employees in organizations where the programs have been adopted. This finding may reflect the fact that the writings about such programs have been targeted at routine assembly and clerical jobs. A comparison with the 1987 results shows a significant increase in the use of job enrichment. Although it is an old idea, it still appears to be growing in popularity.

Self-managing work teams and minienterprise units are used much less frequently than job enrichment. Self-managing work teams are used in 47 percent of the corporations. Where they have been tried, however, they have been applied to only a small percentage of the work force. Minienterprise units are used less frequently than any of the other power-sharing practices; and, like the others, they tend to affect only a small percentage of an organization's employees.

Table 5.2. Power-Sharing Practices Involving Work Redesign.
Percentage of Employees Currently Involved

Innovation/ Program		None 0%	Almost None 1–20%	Some 21–40%	About Half 41–60%	Most 61–80%	Almost All 81–99%	All 100%
Job enrichment	1987	40	38	12	6	2	2	1
or redesign	1990	25	43	23	6	2	0	1
Self-managing	1987	72	20	6	1	0	0	0
work teams	1990	53	37	9	1	0	0	0
Minienterprise	1987	75	18	4	1	1	0	0
units	1990	72	23	3	1	0	1	0

A comparison of the 1987 and 1990 data shows an increase, from 28 percent to 47 percent, in the use of self-managing work teams. Even though the companies do not have large numbers of employees in teams, this is still an impressive increase. Installing such teams involves much more than simply creating a temporary parallel structure. In many cases, equipment has to be moved, employees must be trained, supervisors are reassigned, and a host of other changes have to be made. Nevertheless, significant change has occurred, leaving little question that real increases in power sharing are occurring in the Fortune 1000 companies.

The results do not show a significant increase in the use of mini-enterprise units from 1987 to 1990. This is surprising, in some respects, given the increase in other power-sharing approaches. It may reflect the reality that it simply involves more power sharing and change than most organizations are comfortable with. In addition, this approach is not right for all business, since it fits best in businesses where small independent units are appropriate but does not fit businesses that require large integrated units to deliver services or make products. Still, these units may become more popular in the future, as they become the subject of more writing (Mills, 1991). They are a logical step beyond self-managing teams (Lawler, 1992).

Additional analysis of the data suggests that companies with job enrichment, self-managing work teams, and minienterprise units are more likely to have such parallel structures as quality circles. In other words, a company that engages in one of the more popular employee involvement activities is more likely to try others. Table 5.3 shows, however, that the use of multiple approaches on a large scale is not widespread.

Table 5.3 Power-Sharing Approaches Used with More Than 40 Percent of Employees.[a]

Number of Approaches	Percentage Saying Used with More Than 40% of Employees	
	1987	1990
0	58	52
1	23	28
2	11	13
3	6	4
4	3	3
5 or more	0	1

[a]Seven possible kinds: survey feedback, job enrichment, quality circles, employee participation groups, union-management QWL committees, minienterprise units, self-managing teams.

Only 21 percent of companies have tried two or more of these approaches with over 40 percent of their employees. Therefore, although most companies are doing something to move power downward, few companies are using organizationwide approaches or multiple approaches so that many employees are affected by multiple power-sharing approaches.

Figure 5.1 shows that, in the eyes of our respondents, some decision-making power has been moved to lower levels as a result of companies' employee involvement activities. This finding fits with the popularity of the suggestion-oriented approaches and the increased popularity of job enrichment and work teams.

The data on activities designed to move power downward show that suggestion-type programs have been particularly widely used. Most corporations have at least tried this approach somewhere, probably because such programs are the easiest to install and bring about the least change in organizational power relationships. Nevertheless, the growth of self-managing work teams is perhaps the most significant change and may indicate that a number of companies are going beyond problem-solving approaches.

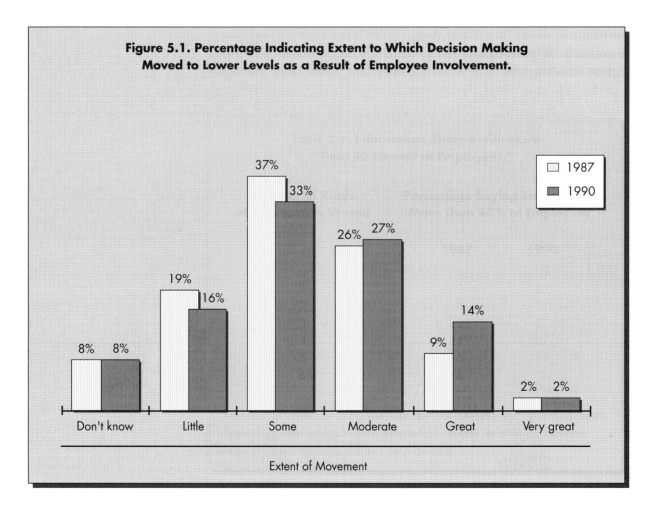

Figure 5.1. Percentage Indicating Extent to Which Decision Making Moved to Lower Levels as a Result of Employee Involvement.

Finally, it is important to note that none of the power-sharing practices listed in Table 5.1 and 5.2 are widely used in most companies. Typically, they cover less than 40 percent of the employees in the companies that use them. This finding strongly suggests that companies are piloting or selectively utilizing these practices, rather than adopting them as basic approaches to organizing and managing.

SECTION 6

Patterns of Information, Knowledge, Rewards, and Power

In this section, we distinguish different organizational approaches to employee involvement on the basis of patterns of involvement practices that companies adopt. Our assumption is that organizations will tend to implement clusters of power-sharing, information, knowledge, and reward practices that have a consistent logic. Therefore, we use a statistical technique called *cluster analysis* to discover sets of organizations that use similar patterns of employee involvement practices. Then we look at how these patterns are reflected in the use of different employee involvement practices. In later sections, we explore how different patterns of employee involvement are related to company policies and types of companies.

A number of scholars have proposed ways of classifying employee involvement practices (for example, see Cotton and others, 1988; Dachler and Wilpert, 1978). Cotton and others distinguish between participation in work decisions, consultative participation (for example, quality circles), short-term participation (for example, during training sessions), informal participation (that is, supervisor-subordinate relations), employee ownership, and representative participation (for example, through works councils). Theoretical typologies are useful in that they help practitioners and researchers consider a variety of alternatives in the design of employee involvement efforts, rather than just one or two types. Nevertheless, there are very few data to support the validity or utility of any of the existing typologies. Therefore, the data-based approach that we take here is quite different from previous approaches and can add important new insights and findings.

Types of Employee Involvement Users. Our cluster analysis suggests that firms can be divided into four basic types of employee involvement users. Three of the four types can be distinguished simply on the basis of their relative levels of activity. We call these *low users, average users,* and *high users* of employee involvement practices. The fourth type, *reward-oriented users,* is distinguished by a tendency to use rewards much more than any other type of employee involvement practice. Sixteen percent of the sample could not be classified with our statistical procedure. This finding suggests that a fairly large number of firms use idiosyncratic patterns of employee involvement practices. Table 6.1 shows the number and percentage of each type of employee involvement user.

Table 6.1. Types of Employee Involvement Users Among Fortune 1000 Firms.		
Type of User	Number of Companies	Percentage of Companies
Low user	112	36
Average user	107	34
High user	23	7
Reward-oriented user	21	7
Not classified	50	16

The finding that three of the four types (representing 77 percent of all cases) can be distinguished simply by level of employee involvement activity is interesting. It indicates that companies that adopt any given power-sharing, information, knowledge, or reward practice to a certain degree, relative to other companies, tend also to adopt other practices to the same relative degree. For example, a company that, relative to other companies, makes heavy use of employee participation groups is likely also to make relatively heavy use of a wide range of other employee involvement practices. Similarly, a company that, relative to other companies, makes light use of employee participation groups is likely also to make relatively light use of other employee involvement practices. This finding suggests an organization discovers that changing one part of the organization requires changing other parts as well. It also supports the idea that the transition to high-involvement management is a systemic change requiring all parts of the organization to be brought into alignment with this management philosophy.

Another implication of the data presented in Table 6.1 is that relatively few companies are heavy users of employee involvement practices in general or reward practices in particular. Some 70 percent of the sample falls into the low user and average user categories. Only 7 percent each belong to the high user and reward-oriented user categories.

As we discuss the use of various employee involvement practices by each type of user, we will characterize the relative level of use in the following way. *Average* means not significantly different from the overall mean for the entire sample; *high* or *low* means different to a statistically significant degree from other groups.

Table 6.2. Patterns of Information Sharing by Type of EI User.

Measure	Low Users	Average Users	High Users	Reward-Oriented Users
Company's operating results	low	average	average	average
Unit operating results	low	average	high	average
Fellow employees' pay	low	average	high	average
New technologies	low	average	high	average
Business plans and goals	low	average	high	average
Competitors' performance	low	average	high	low
Information (index)	3.6	4.3	5.8	4.6

Information-Sharing Practices. Table 6.2 indicates that the use of any one information-sharing practice can be predicted quite well by employee involvement type. Low users of employee involvement are low on every information-sharing practice, and average users are average on every practice. High users are high on every information-sharing practice except disseminating the company's operating results. (The latter is an exception partly because most firms of all types broadly share such operating results.) Reward-oriented users are low on sharing information about competitors' performance but otherwise are average on every information-sharing practice.

We constructed an information index score for each company. This score is the average of the company's scores for the various information-sharing practices. (More information about this and other index scores is found in Resource C.) The index score for the five types of information combined reflects the general pattern we have described. Low users scored 3.6 on a 7-point scale, indicating that the typical low user shared each type of information with a minority of employees (21–40 percent). The average user, at 4.3, shared each type of information with about half of employees (41–60 percent). Reward-oriented users scored marginally higher, at 4.6. High users scored 5.8. This finding indicates that the typical high user is almost to the point on the scale at which each type of information is shared with a great majority (81–99 percent) of employees.

Measure	Low Users	Average Users	High Users	Reward-Oriented Users
				Table 6.3. Patterns of Knowledge by Type of EI User.
Decision making/problem solving	low	average	high	average
Leadership skills	average	average	high	average
Understanding the business	low	average	high	average
Quality skills	low	average	high	average
Team-building skills	low	low	high	average
Job skills	average	average	high	average
Training (index)	2.6	2.9	4.0	3.0

Knowledge. The pattern for training practices shown in Table 6.3 is similar to that for information-sharing practices. Low users are average on training for leadership skills and job skills but are low on every other type of training. Average users are low on providing team-building skills but otherwise are average on every type of skill training. High users are high on every type of training. Reward-oriented users are average on every type of training.

The index score combining all types of training shows a strong relationship to the use of employee involvement. Low users scored 2.6, indicating that the typical low user has provided each type of training within the last three years to a minority of the work force (between the points on the scale corresponding to 1–20 percent and 21–40 percent of employees). Average users and reward-oriented users scored 2.9 and 3.0, respectively, indicating that they trained 21–40 percent of employees within the prior three years. High users scored 4.0, indicating that they included about half (41–60 percent) of their employees on each type of training within the prior three years.

Rewards. Table 6.4 shows that reward-oriented users are high in use of all-salaried pay systems, knowledge-/skill-based pay, profit sharing, individual incentives, and stock ownership. They are average in the use of gainsharing, nonmonetary awards, team incentives, and flexible benefits (no group is relatively high in the use of any of these practices). Low users are low on use of profit sharing, nonmonetary awards, and stock ownership, and they are average on all other measures. Average users

Measure	Low Users	Average Users	High Users	Reward-Oriented Users
All-salaried system	average	average	low	high
Knowledge-/skill-based pay	average	average	average	high
Profit sharing	low	low	high	high
Gainsharing	average	average	average	average
Individual incentives	average	average	average	high
Work-group/team incentives	average	average	average	average
Nonmonetary awards	low	average	average	average
Employee stock ownership plan	low	low	high	high
Flexible benefits	average	average	average	average
Rewards (index)	2.3	2.9	3.1	4.0

Table 6.4. Patterns of Reward System Practices by Type of EI User.

are low on profit sharing and stock ownership and average on all other practices. High users are high only on profit sharing and stock ownership; they are low on use of all-salaried pay systems and average on all other measures.

The overall pattern supports our general finding that many companies adopt a variety of reward practices for reasons other than support of employee involvement. Nevertheless, the fact that a separate cluster of reward-oriented companies has emerged suggests that, for some, rewards are a primary lever for involving employees.

The index score for the nine types of rewards combined shows that the reward-oriented user group is the highest, as expected, at 4.0. This means that, on the average, reward-oriented users cover about half of employees with the typical reward practice. Average users and high users are similar to each other, at 2.9 and 3.1, respectively. This means that they cover 21–40 percent of employees with the typical reward practice. Low users are somewhat lower, at 2.3; they cover 1–20 percent of employees with the typical reward practice.

Power. Two power-sharing practices, self-managing teams and mini-enterprise units, are used to a fairly low degree across all four groups.

Table 6.5. Patterns of Power-Sharing Practices by Type of EI User.

Measure	Low Users	Average Users	High Users	Reward-Oriented Users
Survey feedback	low	average	high	high
Job enrichment	low	low	high	average
Quality circles	low	average	high	average
Participation groups (non-QC)	low	average	high	average
Union-management QWL committees	low	average	high	average
Minienterprise units	average	average	average	average
Self-managing work teams	average	average	average	average
Power sharing (index)	1.8	2.3	3.4	2.9

All groups rate average on these practices. For other measures, the pattern shown in Table 6.5 is similar to that for information-sharing practices and training practices. Low users are relatively low in use of survey feedback, job enrichment, quality circles, other participation groups, and union-management QWL committees. Average users are average in use of all practices except job enrichment, where they are low. High users are high in the use of all five practices. Reward-oriented users are high in use of survey feedback but average in use of all other power-sharing practices.

By comparison with other employee involvement practices, power-sharing practices are the least broadly disseminated among Fortune 1000 firms. The index score for the power-sharing practices shows that high users are the highest once again, with a score of 3.4. This puts high users above the point on the scale corresponding to coverage of 21–40 percent of employees with the typical power-sharing practice. Low users rate 1.8, near the point at which 1–20 percent of the work force is covered with the typical power-sharing practice. Average users and reward-oriented users are in between these points on the scale. Average users rate 2.3, and reward-oriented users rate 2.9 on the index.

Adoption Patterns. We have identified four types of employee involvement users that are suggested by actual patterns of the use of employee involvement practices. Low users are low in the use of two-thirds of all information-sharing, knowledge, reward, and power-sharing practices covered in this study. They rate no higher than average on use of the remaining practices. Average users are even more consistent; they are average on the use of twenty-three of twenty-seven practices. High users are high in the use of almost every practice except rewards, where their level of use is distinctly average. This pattern suggests systemic rather than targeted adoption of employee involvement practices. Companies tend to adopt a variety of information-sharing, knowledge, reward, and power-sharing practices, rather than just adopting one or a smaller number of these practices. The exception to this general pattern is reward-oriented users. They are average on the use of nearly all employee involvement practices except rewards, where their level of use is high for four of seven practices.

PART TWO

The Structure of Employee Involvement Programs

SECTION 7

Approach to Employee Involvement Efforts

The implementation of employee involvement can be a complex process because the objective is to change the way an organization is managed. Many organizational systems need to be changed. Because of this, we focused on how companies go about implementing employee involvement in order to change their approaches to management. To get a sense of how organizations are approaching this change effort, we asked a question concerning the approaches that organizations use in order to facilitate the adoption of employee involvement as a management style.

Table 7.1 presents responses to a question about the use of eight implementation-design features that could be supportive of employee involvement activities. The first four of these implementation practices are

Table 7.1. Implementation Design Features.		
Implementation Design Feature	**Percentage Having**	
	1987	1990
Internal facilitators, trainers, or consulting staff devoted exclusively or primarily to employee involvement activities	58	64
Written management objectives concerning employee involvement activities	50	44
Formal statement of corporate philosophy or policy on employee involvement	49	49
External consultants, trainers, or facilitators for employee involvement activities	46	57
Formal measurement of employee involvement activities	39	31
Separate budget for employee involvement activities	35	32
Manual of procedures on employee involvement	34	26
Assessment of employee involvement implementation in managers' performance reviews	N/A	30

rather widely adopted. Most organizations with employee involvement activities use both internal and external consultants, trainers, and facilitators. The use of external consultants shows a significant increase over the 1987 results. Some increase is also reported in the use of internal facilitators.

One reasonable interpretation here is that organizations are increasingly finding that employee involvement is difficult to install and that there is a role for experts in this area. This is not surprising, given the expertise needed to start and run such programs as gainsharing and quality circles. There also seem to be a growing number of consultants who have expertise in employee involvement, and a number of consulting firms have developed training programs to support employee involvement change efforts. Clearly, expertise concerning employee involvement needs to be developed in an organization, and a reasonable way to do this is to use consultants and internal staff experts. In the long term, however, the key to success probably is to transfer these skills, so that they become resident in the managers themselves and become a standard way of doing business (Mohrman and others, 1989).

Almost half the companies utilize a formal statement of corporate philosophy or policy on employee involvement. Written management objectives are used in 44 percent of companies, down from 50 percent in 1987. Both these approaches provide direction and a sense of intent for the transition to high involvement. A philosophy statement can provide an umbrella position within which the organization and its members can strive to bring systems and behaviors into alignment. Objectives can provide milestones and a sense of priority.

As in our 1987 survey, the least frequently adopted implementation practices are assessment in performance reviews, formal measurement, use of a separate budget, and use of a manual of procedures on employee involvement.

The use of formal manuals shows a significant decrease between 1987 and 1990. The lack of a manual may reflect the desire to allow parts of organizations to invent their own programs and do things that fit the local environment. Consultants working on employee involvement frequently recommend this practice. It may also reflect the increasing use of consultants and facilitators to provide appropriate expertise.

The lack of a separate budget can be interpreted positively or negatively. It can be seen as positive if it signals that employee involvement is not a special activity but rather a regular, ongoing activity of the organization. Many organizations have a history of special "flavor of the month" programs, with their own budgets. The programs often disappear when their budgets disappear. Given the extra training and other activities needed to start employee involvement, however, the lack of a separate budget can be seen as a lack of real support for the start of employee involvement activities.

Formal measurement of employee involvement activities shows a decrease from 1987 to 1990. Measurement of activities is clearly one way to indicate strong support for doing something. Particularly if measurement is tied to rewards for managers implementing employee involvement, as it is in 30 percent of the companies, it can be an effective way to motivate action. Nevertheless, it runs the risk of encouraging people to go through the motions of starting activities in order to meet specific measurement criteria. This is a particularly great risk when rewards are tied to the measures. There is evidence that this has happened in quality circle programs. Managers have started circles just to meet the objective of having a certain number of them operating (Lawler and Mohrman, 1985). Installing employee involvement just to meet an objective works against these activities' becoming a way of life and a way of management based on internal commitment. Instead, it can create a formal, compliance-driven approach that is never well institutionalized.

Overall, it is interesting that no specific approach to implementation is adopted by an overwhelming number of organizations. Instead, it seems that there are a number of commonly used approaches, and most companies adopt more than one. This pattern of adoption probably reflects the diversity of the conditions in the companies studied, as well as a large amount of uncertainty about how to produce a large-scale organizational change (Mohrman and others, 1989).

SECTION 8

Personnel Policies and Practices Facilitating Employee Involvement

A number of personnel policies and practices can support employee involvement. Table 8.1 lists the major practices and shows the extent to which they have been adopted. The argument in favor of these practices as part of an employee involvement management approach is that they provide an organizational context and support for employee involvement. By themselves, they do not necessarily represent a significant move to employee involvement, but the values and goals of these policies fit with the values and goals of employee involvement. Moreover, in some cases these policies and practices go beyond providing an organizational context and actually do provide the kinds of power and skills that directly support employee involvement.

Employee security is frequently suggested as a necessary or at least desirable practice by proponents of gainsharing, union-management quality of work life efforts, and other employee involvement approaches

(Rosow and Zager, 1984). The reasoning behind this is straightforward. It can help alleviate individuals' concerns about working themselves out of a job, because performance improves as a result of employee involvement. It also has the potential for freeing people to be more innovative and committed to careers in particular organizations. Nevertheless, fewer than one-third of the companies cover over 40 percent of their employees with employment security statements. At the other extreme, 47 percent cover none of their employees. Clearly, this is a practice on which organizations differ, perhaps in part because of differences in the economic environments they face. Comparison between the 1987 and the 1990 data shows a small drop in the number of employees covered by employment security practices. This finding may reflect the turbulent environment that many companies faced in the late 1980s.

Employee input to hiring decisions is used to some degree by about two-thirds of the organizations, but those who do use it do not cover most employees. A strong argument can be made for its contribution to employee involvement. First, it is a way to help ensure that people supportive of employee involvement are hired. It gives applicants a realistic preview of what involvement is like and, as a result, may discourage those who do not like it from taking jobs. It also gives employees a chance to

Table 8.1. Percentage of Employees Covered by EI-Related Personnel Policies/Practices.

		None 0%	Almost None 1–20%	Some 21–40%	More Than 40% 41–100%
Employment security	1987	46	15	6	33
	1990	47	20	6	27
Hiring based partly on	1987	33	47	13	7
employee input	1990	33	44	15	8
Flextime	1987	31	40	16	13
	1990	18	44	18	20
Cross-training	1987	5	30	36	29
	1990	3	29	41	27
Realistic job preview/portrayal	1987	9	14	16	61
to potential hires	1990	11	27	16	47
Suggestion system	1987	17	17	15	51
	1990	14	24	14	48

assess whether an applicant will fit into the organization. Second, it is a participative practice in its own right and a valid way to move one type of power downward in an organization. A comparison of the 1987 and 1990 results shows no significant change in its use. It continues to enjoy limited use.

Flextime is another practice that is participative in its own right, since it allows individuals to make important decisions about a part of their work situation. It is used by 82 percent of the companies, but those companies that do use it tend to cover only a small part of the work force. It does appear to be increasing in popularity; the percentage using it increased from 69 percent to 82 percent.

Cross-training enables individuals to learn about different parts of the organization and about how their total work units operate. It is often done in conjunction with the installation of self-managing work teams and skill-based pay. The results indicate that most organizations do cross-train employees, but that substantially less than half of employees are cross-trained. This lack of exposure to different work activities may limit the ability of individuals to participate in workplace decision making and to develop their careers. A comparison between the 1987 and 1990 results shows no significant change in the number of employees covered by cross-training. This is inconsistent with the increased use of self-managing teams and skill-based pay, but it fits with the earlier finding that these firms have not increased their training activities.

Realistic job previews are often implemented as a way to ensure that job applicants understand in advance the kind of work culture they are entering (Premack and Wanous, 1985). This is particularly important in the case of an organization that practices employee involvement because it places different demands on employees from those in traditional work settings. The results suggest that this hiring technique is used by almost 90 percent of the companies studied; few use it for all employees, however. A comparison between the 1987 and 1990 results shows little change in the number of companies doing realistic job previews, but there is a suggestion in the data that their use is somewhat less widespread within those companies that use them.

Finally, suggestion systems are a traditional way to move information and ideas upward in an organization. As can be seen in Table 8.1, they continue to be used by most organizations (86 percent). Although suggestion systems are one approach to involvement, they are very limited in the amount and kind of involvement they offer. It is also debatable whether an individually oriented suggestion system, especially when rewards are attached, can happily coexist with a group-oriented involvement design (Lawler, 1990). There is a possible conflict between helping the group and helping oneself. In situations where groups are not used, suggestion systems may be a positive force and an important contributor to employee involvement. Their continued popularity suggests that they are viable forms of participation.

Table 8.2 shows the percentage of companies applying these six practices to at least 40 percent of employees. Twenty percent of the organizations are using none of these practices with 40 percent or more of their employees. Thirty-one percent of companies, however, are applying at least three of these practices to 40 percent or more of their employees, indicating that they have a relatively strong commitment to personnel practices that support employee involvement. Therefore, it appears that a significant number of companies have some of the basic personnel policies that support employee involvement. For them, adopting employee involvement should be much easier than it is for other companies.

Table 8.3 presents information about how the use of these practices differs across the four types of employee involvement users identified earlier. The overall pattern in use of the personnel practices and policies is very similar to the pattern for the use of employee involvement practices. High users are high in the use of all these personnel practices and policies. Average users are average in use of all practices and policies. Reward-oriented users are also average in the use of all practices. Low users are average in the use of employment security and flextime and

Table 8.2. Number of EI-Related Personnel Practices Used with at Least 40 Percent of Employees.[a]

Number of Approaches	Percentage Saying Used with at Least 40% of Employees
	1990
0	20
1	30
2	19
3	18
4	11
5	2
6	0

[a]Six possible kinds: employment security, employee input to hiring, flextime, cross-training, realistic job preview, suggestion system.

Table 8.3. Personnel Policies/Practices by Type of EI User.

Measure	Low Users	Average Users	High Users	Reward-Oriented Users
Employment security	average	average	high	average
Hiring with employee input	low	average	high	average
Flextime	average	average	high	average
Cross-training	low	average	high	average
Realistic job preview	low	average	high	average
Suggestion system	low	average	high	average

low in the use of the other four policies and practices. The overall level of use of employee involvement practices thus predicts the level of use of these personnel policies and practices.

SECTION 9

Implementing Employee Involvement: Facilitators and Barriers

Installing employee involvement is a complex process. It may encounter a number of obstacles, and it needs support. Identifying critical facilitators of and barriers to employment involvement is necessary, to gain an understanding of what it takes to implement employee involvement successfully.

The responses to a question concerning the degree to which a number of organizational conditions currently facilitate employee involvement activities are shown in Table 9.1. One condition stands out as an important facilitator or supporter: 50 percent of respondents view support by top management as a great or very great facilitator of employee involvement in the organization. Support by middle management is rated as the second-greatest facilitator, but it is rated much lower than support by senior management.

A comparison between the 1987 and 1990 responses shows a significant drop in the degree to which middle managers and first-line supervisors are seen as facilitators. This may reflect the realization that in some cases these managers lose when employee involvement programs are instituted. They often have to change their behavior significantly and may lose their jobs because, typically, fewer supervisors and levels of management are needed with self-managing work teams and other employee involvement structures (Wellins, Byham, and Wilson, 1991; Lawler, 1992). Therefore, although they may support involvement programs initially, it is reasonable to expect some middle managers and lower-level managers to become much less supportive after it is clear how the programs will affect them.

Lower ratings are given to the availability of resources and employment security in 1990, as compared to the 1987 survey. This may well reflect difficult economic times in most companies during the late 1980s.

Support from top management is a particularly strong facilitator in companies identified as high users of employee involvement. In many respects, this is hardly surprising, since it is hard in a hierarchical organization to produce significant change without the support of top management. This is not to say that bottom-up change may not be desirable or, to some degree, possible (for example, see Beer, Eisenstat, and

Table 9.1. Conditions Facilitating Employee Involvement.

To What Extent, if at All, Is Each of the Following Conditions Currently a Facilitator of Employee Involvement in Your Corporation?

Condition	Percentage Saying a Great or Very Great Facilitator[a]	
	1987	1990
Support by top management	55	50
Support by middle management	39	26
Support by first-line supervisors	33	19
Availability of resources (money, personnel, etc.) for employee involvement activities	28	21
Decentralization of decision-making authority	22	21
Employment security	17	9
Third-party consultation	13	15
Monetary rewards for employee involvement activity	7	7

[a]Responded 4 or 5 on 5-point extent scale: 1=little or no extent; 5=very great extent; "no basis to judge" also a possible response.

Spector, 1990). Indeed, unless significant support develops at lower levels in the organization, there is a real danger than meaningful change will never be sustained (Mohrman and others, 1989). Nevertheless, few would deny that employee involvement is easier to implement and sustain when top management is supportive, or that top management can do a great deal to facilitate the change process.

Table 9.2 focuses on how frequently barriers are mentioned by organizations that have employee involvement programs. The table shows the percentage of respondents that report certain conditions were great obstacles or very great obstacles to employee involvement. The condition that stands out in this table is short-term performance pressure. Much of the writing on employee involvement stresses that changing to employee involvement is a long-term process that may not produce short-term results (for example, see Lawler, 1986, 1992). In addition, there can be significant start-up costs associated with employee involvement. Consultants, new staff groups, and training programs all cost money. In

Table 9.2. Barriers to Employee Involvement.
To What Extent, if at All, Is Each of the Following
Conditions Currently a Barrier to EI Efforts?

Condition	Percentage Saying a Great or Very Great Obstacle[a]	
	1987	1990
Short-term performance pressure	43	46
Lack of a champion for employee involvement	26	20
Lack of a long-term strategy	25	28
Unclear employee involvement objectives	21	25
Lack of tangible improvements (e.g., dollar savings)	20	12
Centralization of decision-making authority	17	18
Management culture opposed to employee involvement	15	12
Worsened business conditions	14	14
Lack of coordination of employee involvement programs with other programs	12	17
Turnover in top management	6	5

[a]Responded 4 or 5 on 5-point extent scale: 1=little or no extent; 5=very great extent; "no basis to judge" also a possible response.

a business environment where quarterly earnings reports are given a great deal of attention, it is not surprising that short-term performance pressures are rated as the major obstacle.

Two "strategy" items are rated as the next two greatest obstacles. This finding may reflect the fact that some companies have started employee involvement because it is "the thing to do." A long-term strategy and clear objectives are critical ingredients if such programs are to be sustained and have long-term positive impacts on organizations.

The other conditions listed are less frequently identified as important obstacles, but they may still be important in organizations that experience them. For example, the lack of a champion is of great importance in 20 percent of the companies. This suggests that it is not always easy to find someone willing to take on this role in an organization.

Table 9.3. Facilitators of and Barriers to Employee Involvement by Type of EI User.

Measure	Low Users	Average Users	High Users	Reward-Oriented Users
Facilitators[a]				
Support by top management	low	average	high	average
Decentralization of decision-making authority	average	average	high	average
Barriers				
Short-term performance pressures	average	average	low	average
Lack of a champion for employee involvement	high	average	low	average
Unclear employee involvement objectives	high	average	average	average
Lack of long-term strategy	high	average	low	average
Management culture	high	average	average	average

[a]Facilitators and barriers not mentioned show no significant differences (that is, are average for all types of users).

A comparison between the 1987 and 1990 data shows little significant change. The largest drop is in the item "lack of tangible improvements." Only 12 percent now see this as a great obstacle. One possibility is that as programs in companies have matured, they have produced tangible results. It is also possible that employee involvement is now the "thing to do," and so results are not necessary. In either case, this result suggests that we will see further adoption of employee involvement practices in the future.

Overall, the data on obstacles to implementation suggest that implementation is primarily a matter of being willing to make the commitment to producing organizational change. It is not a matter of lack of technology, knowledge, or resources. Rather, it is an issue of making the commitment to a difficult long-term change process. To be successful in the change process requires extensive commitment on the part of employees at all levels and patience on the part of senior management. Champions are also needed, to see a well-developed program through to its end regardless of short-term competitive pressure.

Different types of employee involvement users do not differ a great deal in the degree to which different facilitators are operative in their firms. As Table 9.3 indicates, there are significant differences only on two facilitators: support by top management, and decentralization of decision-making authority. Both of these are high for high users and average for average users and reward-oriented users. Low users report low support from top management and average decentralization.

Table 9.3 indicates differences between types of employee involvement users on five of the ten barriers to employee involvement. Low users are much more likely than other groups to cite lack of a champion, unclear objectives, lack of a long-term strategy, and a hostile management culture. High users are less likely to report that short-term performance pressure, lack of a champion, and lack of a long-term strategy are barriers to employee involvement efforts. Average users and reward-oriented users report a consistently average experience on all these measures.

The overall pattern reinforces our previous comments about the relative importance of certain facilitators and barriers. In general, those facilitators and barriers that are most often cited as important are also the ones that best differentiate high users from low users.

PART THREE

Results of
Employee Involvement
Programs

SECTION 10

Success of Reward System Programs

Those companies using the reward system practices most commonly associated with employee involvement programs were asked to rate the success of these practices in enhancing organizational performance. Table 10.1 presents the results of the reward system ratings for 1990. These questions were not asked in the 1987 survey. Overall, the ratings are extremely positive. All the pay-for-performance systems are rated as quite successful. No system was rated as unsuccessful by more than 7 percent of the companies, an impressively low rate of failure.

The highest success ratings go to profit sharing and employee stock ownership. These also happen to be the plans that have been adopted for the longest period—an average of thirteen years in the case of profit sharing, and ten years in the case of employee stock ownership. Apparently, these plans are well established in the Fortune 1000 and are clearly rated as quite successful.

Table 10.1. Percentage Indicating Success of Reward System Practices.

	Very Unsuccessful	Unsuccessful	Undecided	Successful	Very Successful
All-salaried pay systems	0	2	23	59	17
Knowledge-/skill-based pay	3	3	35	54	6
Profit sharing	0	4	25	45	26
Gainsharing	1	3	43	42	12
Individual incentives	2	5	19	62	12
Work-group or team incentives	0	5	34	51	10
Nonmonetary recognition awards for performance	0	2	18	63	17
Employee stock ownership plan	1	4	23	49	23
Flexible, cafeteria-style benefits	2	2	31	42	24

Gainsharing is a much newer practice. The average company had been using it just over three years. Therefore, it is not surprising to find that more respondents are undecided with respect to its success. Nevertheless, 54 percent rated it as either successful or very successful, and only 4 percent rated it as unsuccessful or very unsuccessful. This is generally in line with results of other studies that have actually measured the quantitative success of gainsharing (see, for example, O'Dell, 1987; U.S. General Accounting Office, 1981). These studies tend to find success rates of 60 to 70 percent.

Work-group or team incentives are also rated as quite successful. Again, there is a relatively large percentage of ratings in the undecided category, but few respondents report failure. These programs have been around an average of six years. Overall, they seem to be working well.

The results for nonmonetary recognition rewards are also quite favorable. Eighty percent rate them as successful or very successful. These programs clearly have been around for a considerable time; they average fifteen years in use. Apparently, most of these programs have not been introduced as part of recent movements toward employee involvement. Instead, they are well-established efforts to recognize outstanding employee performance in a wide range of areas. In some cases, of course, they may have been adapted or developed to help support an employee involvement or total quality effort. Their relatively high reported success rate is quite impressive.

Companies reporting on all-salaried pay systems also indicate a high level of success. Only 2 percent report that they are unsuccessful. These are relatively well-established programs that have been in use an average of twelve years.

Most knowledge- or skill-based pay programs are relatively new (an average of four years old) but are nevertheless seen as quite successful. Sixty percent of the companies report that their programs are successful. Given the newness of this technology and its evolution, this seems a relatively high success rate.

Flexible benefits are the newest of the reward system practices. The typical company has had a flexible benefit program for just under three years. The reported success rate, however, is very high, topping 65 percent. Apparently, this reward system practice is proving quite effective. One possible explanation for the high success rate is that even though most of the plans were recently adopted, a lot of effort has been put into developing the technology of flexible benefits. A number of consulting firms have developed good plans, and companies, as a result, can move ahead with these programs without having to do a great deal of their own developmental work (Bloom and Trahan, 1986). Therefore companies can have a high probability of success when they adopt flexible benefit programs, even though they may be doing something new and different.

The overall results reported in Table 10.1 are quite impressive. The respondents clearly feel that these reward system practices are important contributors to organizational performance. This helps explain why there is growth in the adoption of flexible benefits, skill-based pay, and gainsharing.

SECTION 11

Success of Power-Sharing Programs

Users of the seven power-sharing programs discussed in Section 5 were asked to evaluate their success in helping improve organizational performance. The results are summarized in Table 11.1. The pattern of responses is very similar to the results obtained in our 1987 study. All of the programs are seen as successful. They were rated successful or very successful by a majority of the respondents. No approach was rated unsuccessful by more than 12 percent of respondents, although a number of respondents indicated that they were undecided about the level of success.

Table 11.1. Percentage Indicating Success of Power-Sharing Programs.

		Very Unsuccessful	Unsuccessful	Undecided	Successful	Very Successful
Survey feedback	1987	1	2	28	57	12
	1990	0	5	25	60	10
Quality circles	1987	0	5	27	54	13
	1990	1	11	36	48	4
Participation groups other than QCs	1987	1	3	28	53	16
	1990	1	0	26	62	11
Union-management QWL committees	1987	0	9	44	40	8
	1990	0	2	48	46	4
Job enrichment or redesign	1987	0	3	46	46	5
	1990	0	4	40	49	7
Self-managing work teams	1987	0	1	46	45	8
	1990	1	0	39	44	16
Minienterprise units	1987	0	3	41	48	8
	1990	0	0	47	45	8

The most favorable ratings went to survey feedback and employee participation groups. As noted earlier, both of these approaches are parallel participation vehicles that take people out of their traditional work roles for discussions of how the workplace can be improved. They require no fundamental change in the management style of the organization. They are relatively easy to implement in all kinds of organizations and, as research has shown, can produce positive results in most situations (Lawler, 1986).

Quality circles are seen as less successful than survey feedback and participation groups. This represents a significant change from 1987, when they were seen as comparable. What explains the less favorable ratings for quality circles? A number of articles have pointed out the transitory nature of their success and have warned that they may not be a good long-term approach to employee involvement (Lawler and Mohrman, 1985). Apparently, a number of companies are finding that this is true. In addition, during the middle 1980s, quality circles became a fad, and it is possible that some of the drop in their success rating is due to overuse and misuse.

Union-management quality of work life (QWL) committees also get relatively low success ratings. It should be noted that this lower rating is only relative; 50 percent of union-management QWL efforts were rated successful or very successful, and only 2 percent were rated unsuccessful. Typically, they are the most complicated parallel structures to design, implement, and manage because they must be jointly managed by unions and managements that previously have dealt with each other in a primarily adversarial mode (Herrick, 1990). Furthermore, many of these structures are being established in old-line unionized industries during very difficult economic times that involve downsizing, layoffs, and plant shutdowns and consolidations. Dealing in a cooperative, problem-solving way constitutes breaking important new ground and involves using and developing new skills. Success is by no means assured and may be difficult to assess with these conditions.

Job enrichment, work teams and minienterprise units are quite different from parallel organization activities. They often require major structural changes in other design elements of the organization (Wellins, Byham, and Wilson, 1991; Lawler, 1992). Therefore, they are more difficult to implement and operate successfully. Nevertheless, the companies that report having tried them generally say that they are successful, and so even though they often are seen as difficult and demanding to install, they appear to be successful once installed. Particularly impressive is the increased success rate reported for self-managing teams. The 1990 data show an increase in the degree to which they are rated as very successful. Apparently, some of the companies that have adopted them have found them very powerful approaches to employee involvement. This may help explain why they are being adopted by more companies and suggests that their use will continue to increase.

The high success ratings given to all the employee involvement programs that emphasize power sharing is quite impressive. Obviously there are many satisfied users. This is especially significant, given the newness of some of the practices and the fact that, as technologies, they are not well developed. Once they are better developed and understood, they may be seen as even more effective.

SECTION 12

Results of Employee Involvement Programs

A key question with respect to any large-scale organizational change effort concerns its impact on organizational effectiveness. Effectiveness can be defined in two ways: change in internal operating processes, and change in operating results. Table 12.1 looks at the first of these. It presents the results of a question that asked to what extent employee involvement activities have resulted in a series of improvements in important internal operating processes and business conditions.

Table 12.1. Percentage Indicating at Least Some Improvement in Internal Business Conditions as a Result of Employee Involvement.

Internal Business Conditions	Percentage Saying Improved at Least Some[a]	
	1987	1990
Increased employee trust in management	79	66
Improved organizational processes and procedures	76	75
Improved management decision making	74	69
Improved implementation of technology	66	60
Improved employee safety/health	55	48
Improved union-management relations	43	47
Eliminated layers of management or supervision	38	50
Changed management style to one that is more participatory	79	78

[a]Responded 2, 3, 4, or 5 on 5-point extent scale: 1=little or no extent; 5=very great extent; "no basis to judge" also a possible response.

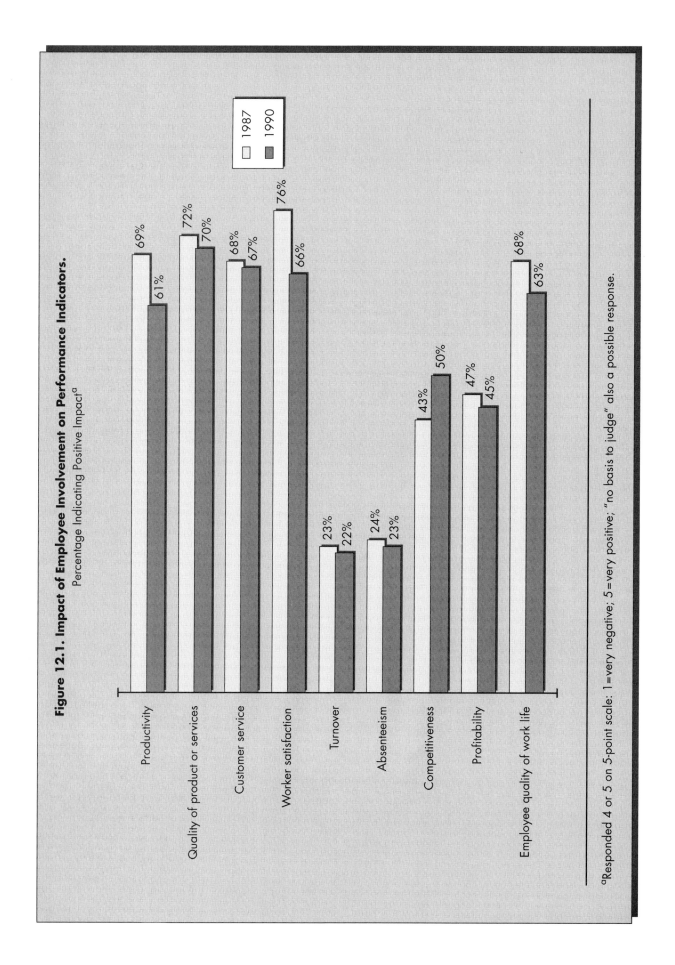

Figure 12.1. Impact of Employee Involvement on Performance Indicators.
Percentage Indicating Positive Impact[a]

Productivity — 69% / 61%
Quality of product or services — 72% / 70%
Customer service — 68% / 67%
Worker satisfaction — 76% / 66%
Turnover — 23% / 22%
Absenteeism — 24% / 23%
Competitiveness — 43% / 50%
Profitability — 47% / 45%
Employee quality of work life — 68% / 63%

1987 / 1990

[a]Responded 4 or 5 on 5-point scale: 1=very negative; 5=very positive; "no basis to judge" also a possible response.

There is considerable variation in the degree to which these internal operations have improved. The greatest improvement is reported in five areas: participatory management, technology implementation, trust, management decision making, and organizational processes and procedures. The result is generally consistent with arguments made in favor of employee involvement. These gains also fit with the type of employee involvement activities more frequently implemented—parallel problem solving. The most common outcome of parallel activities is suggestions on how to improve operations and decision making. Parallel processes can also be used to select new technologies and to make recommendations about their implementation. When the suggestions are listened to and implemented, they can increase trust in management.

The most interesting change from 1987 to 1990 concerns an increase in the likelihood that layers of management will be eliminated. Eliminating layers of management is difficult to do and is not likely to result from parallel participation approaches. Substantial reduction, however, does tend to be associated with self-managing teams and minienterprise units (Lawler, 1992). As discussed earlier, these are being used with greater frequency. One outcome of the greater use of such practices may be a greater tendency for organizations to eliminate management layers. When employee involvement activities involving teams and mini-enterprise units become more common and mature, they may produce further reductions in layers of management.

The significant decline (79 percent to 66 percent) in the degree to which employee involvement programs are producing increased trust in management is difficult to explain. It may be that, as they mature, the programs reveal some of the weaknesses of management, or perhaps the lack of a clear direction for the programs becomes obvious. There may be some disappointment in the unwillingness of some companies to go beyond parallel organization approaches and expand the programs to cover all employees. Finally, the decline may simply be due to the turbulent economic times and to a general decrease in trust as a result of business failures, downsizings, mergers, and consolidations.

In a second question on effectiveness, companies were asked whether employee involvement activities had a positive impact on a number of performance indicators. As shown in Figure 12.1, the results suggest that employee involvement produces a win-win scenario—that is, life is better for employees, and operating results are better for organizations as a result of employee involvement. According to the respondents, worker satisfaction has gone up, as has the quality of work life. Quality, service, and productivity are reported improved as a result of employee involvement efforts in about two-thirds of the companies. Approximately one-half of the companies also report that profitability and competitiveness have improved. Only about one-quarter of the companies, however, report that absenteeism and turnover have dropped. Since these outcomes are typically linked to satisfaction and to the quality of work life, it is surprising that they are not seen as improving in more cases.

A comparison between the 1987 and 1990 data shows some interesting differences. Although the results are generally the same, the 1990 respondents are somewhat less likely to see employee involvement as a positive factor in affecting worker satisfaction and the quality of work life. This may well reflect an increasing focus on the importance of organizational effectiveness and the realization that employee involvement does not have a positive effect on all employees and managers. As we mentioned earlier, it can affect managers negatively, and it may also require employees to change in ways that are not comfortable for them. Nevertheless, the finding that competitiveness is increasingly seen as being aided is important, since competitiveness is critical in today's business environment and is the only way to safeguard employment in the long term.

The results suggest that employee involvement has led to important improvements in organizations that adopt it. These data are similar to the data reported earlier on the success of specific approaches, such as self-managing work teams and gainsharing programs. The data indicate that the survey respondents believe employee involvement is a viable way to improve organizational performance. These results are consistent with the findings of a number of comprehensive reviews of the available research on employee involvement (for example, Blinder, 1990; Golembiewski and Sun, 1990; Heil, 1991).

Effects for Different Types of Employee Involvement Users.   The effects of employee involvement efforts that are experienced by different types of users are shown in Table 12.2. The four types of users report different levels of impact of employee involvement efforts on three performance indicators: productivity, quality of products or services, and absenteeism. The high users report high impact of their employee involvement efforts on productivity and quality, but only an average impact on absenteeism. Both low users and average users report average effects on all three measures. This finding suggests that some threshold in employee involvement adoptions may need to be reached before a firm experiences a performance impact from its efforts. In a difference from the pattern reported elsewhere, reward-oriented users were low rather than average in reported impact of employee involvement on productivity and absenteeism.

The pattern with respect to internal business conditions is also shown in Table 12.2. There are significant differences on nine of the ten indicators. Low users report that their employee involvement efforts have less impact than for the other groups on all nine of these indicators. High users experience a high impact of their employee involvement activities

Measure	Low Users	Average Users	High Users	Reward-Oriented Users
Performance Impact				
Productivity	average	average	high	low
Quality of products/services	average	average	high	average
Absenteeism	average	average	average	low
Changes in Business Environment				
Improved implementation of technology	low	average	average	average
Changed management style	low	average	average	average
Improved union-management relations	low	average	average	average
Moving decision making lower	low	average	average	average
Moving performance-based rewards lower in organization	low	average	average	average
Broadened skill development	low	average	high	average
Increased employee trust	low	average	high	average
Improved management decisions	low	average	high	average
Improved organizational processes and procedures	low	average	average	average

Table 12.2 Effects of Employee Involvement by Type of EI User.

on broadened skill development, increased employee trust, and improved management decisions, but not on other indicators. Average users and reward-oriented users report an average impact on these conditions in all cases. Thus it appears that the level and type of employee involvement activity creates effects in somewhat different ways for performance indicators and internal business conditions. The latter appear to be somewhat more sensitive to the overall level of employee involvement activity in the firm.

Effects of Employee Involvement Practices on Firm Esteem. An additional analysis of the effects of adopting employee involvement practices examined the relationship between level of employee involvement adoption and ratings received in *Fortune* magazine's 1990 listing of "Most Admired Companies" (Smith, 1990). This listing provides representatives of the business community with the opportunity to rate one another on the fairly vague standard of "admirability."

Scores on these ratings are related to a firm's long-term financial performance and size—attributes that most executives find admirable. Nevertheless, the ratings also reflect institutionalized standards of acceptable corporate conduct and the degree to which the company represents "best practice" to other firms. Thus, pharmaceutical maker Merck is consistently placed at or near the top of the ratings, even though it is not the largest or the most profitable U.S. company, and highly profitable cigarette maker Philip Morris has plummeted in the rankings as smoking has become less and less socially acceptable. A high correlation between ranking on the most admired list and use of employee involvement practices would suggest that employee involvement practices are one of the types of practices that large corporations find admirable.

Correlations between the ratings and the use of employee involvement are shown in Table 12.3. (We were able to match this information for 118 firms in our sample.) We used the overall index score and index scores for each element of employee involvement (information, knowledge, rewards, and power) to represent the level of use of employee involvement practices (see Resource C for more information about these indices). We correlated the index scores with both the raw score and the within-industry rank for the *Fortune* listing.

Table 12.3. Relationship Between Use of EI Practices and *Fortune's* "Most Admired Companies" List.		
Employee Involvement Measure	**1990 Most-Admired-List Rating**	
	Raw Score	Rank Within Industry
Employee involvement (index)	**	*
Information (index)		
Training (index)	**	*
Rewards (index)		
Power (index)	*	*

Correlation: * = weak but significant ($p \leq .05$)
               ** = moderate relationship ($p \leq .01$)
N = 118

The pattern is the same for both measures of esteem, although the correlations are slightly higher for the raw scores than for rank within industry. The correlations are statistically significant and moderately strong (greater than .20) for overall index of employee involvement practices and for the training (knowledge) and power indices. The more favorable the ranking, the higher the use of employee involvement practices. The correlations were not significant between the information index or the rewards index and the *Fortune* ratings. The level of information sharing may be less apparent to outside observers than the level of training or use of power-sharing innovations. The use of reward innovations supporting employee involvement is not associated with high external regard.

We examined the correlations of all specific employee involvement practices and the esteem ratings. The results indicate that although most kinds of training are significantly correlated with the ratings, job skills training has an especially high impact. The correlation between within-industry score and the level of job skills training is significant ($r = .41$). Interestingly, the power practices associated with a high reputation are the parallel organization practices (for example, participation groups, survey feedback). The use of self-managing teams and minienterprise units is unrelated to the *Fortune* esteem ratings, perhaps because the overall level of use of these practices is so low in these firms.

In general, it appears that firms using employee involvement practices believe that these practices have a wide variety of positive effects on performance and internal business conditions. Differences in effects between firms are related to type of employee involvement user. Finally, the reputation of the firm is related to its level of use of employee involvement practices, especially training and power-sharing practices.

PART FOUR

Who Adopts Employee Involvement Programs?

SECTION 13

Organizational Characteristics of the Adopters

In this section, we look at the organizational characteristics of firms that use employee involvement practices. Specifically, we look at the influence on adoption of organizational size, service versus manufacturing, and type of industry.

Organizational Size.   In general, organizational size is one of the best predictors of the adoption of innovations of all kinds (Rogers, 1983). Large firms are more likely to adopt most innovations. There are a variety of explanations for this. For example, large firms tend to have more slack resources (that is, resources above those needed for survival), which allows them to fund innovations. Large firms also tend to be complex and diverse, which can increase the number of places where innovations can arise. Corporate staff groups of various kinds that champion innovations are also more common in large firms.

It can be argued, however, that large organizational size may be either a positive or a negative factor in the establishment of employee involvement innovations. Large firms are better able to afford employee involvement innovations, and large firms may experience more of a need to adopt employee involvement practices to overcome some of the liabilities of size. Large firms may experience motivational problems because it is hard for employees and managers to see the impact of their efforts on the corporation as a whole, and employee involvement practices can be seen as a way to compensate for this problem. Large firms also tend to rely more on formal, bureaucratic tools to manage their complexity, and employee involvement can be seen as a means of counteracting the tendency of large firms to become rigid. In addition, organizational size is correlated with heavy foreign competition and decreasing product life cycles, two competitive forces that are correlated with the adoption of employee involvement practices (see Section 15). What works against successful implementation of EI in large organizations is the difficulty of disseminating the practices that one part of a large company adopts. Formal, bureaucratic structures and rigid staff groups can interfere with the dissemination of even successful employee involvement efforts. Moreover, it is often difficult for employees in large organizations to believe that conditions can really change, and that this effort is not just another of the many programs that come and go in most large firms.

Table 13.1 indicates that, in general, organizational size is positively related to the adoption of employee involvement practices. Here, we are measuring firm size in terms of the number of employees in the United States. The larger the firm, the more likely it is to share information about units' operating results, business plans and goals, and competitors' performance. This pattern suggests that larger firms are more likely than smaller firms to focus employee attention on the unit level. Larger firms are also more likely to provide job skills training, as well as training in group decision making, leadership, and team building. In part, this probably reflects the greater role of the training function in larger firms. Three reward practices—gainsharing, nonmonetary recognition awards, and employee stock ownership plans—are also more common in large firms. The use of gainsharing in particular is consistent with the attempt to administer the corporation as a set of smaller and more manageable units. Larger firms are more likely to adopt six of the seven power-sharing practices, and they are especially likely to use survey feedback and quality circles. Larger firms also tend to have been using all the reward and power-sharing practices, except gainsharing and the all-salaried work force, for a longer period. In general, then, organizational size is a good predictor of the adoption of employee involvement practices.

Table 13.1. Firm Size and EI Practices.

Firm Size Is Significantly and Positively Correlated
with Use of the Following Practices:

Information	Unit operating results
	Business plans/goals
	Competitors' performance
Knowledge	Group decision making/problem solving
	Leadership
	Team building
	Job skills
Rewards	Gainsharing
	Nonmonetary recognition awards
	Employee stock ownership plans
Power	Survey feedback
	Job enrichment/redesign
	Quality circles
	Employee participation groups
	Union-management QWL committees
	Self-managing teams

We look more closely at the relationship between firm size and the structure of employee involvement efforts in Table 13.2. Here, we see that there are no differences in who acted as the organization's stimulus for adoption of employee involvement practices. The only difference in reasons for implementation is that larger firms are more likely to adopt employee involvement for ethical or value reasons. It is interesting that staff groups, which typically are larger and more professional in larger firms, are not more of a stimulus source for employee involvement in larger firms.

The major difference between large and small firms is in implementation procedures. These tend to be much more formal in large firms, in keeping with their more bureaucratic structure. Specifically, larger companies are more likely to use a philosophy or policy statement on employee involvement, a procedures manual, written management objectives, formal measurement of employee involvement activities, and both internal and external consultants. There are no differences in projected changes in spending on employee involvement or in barriers to the adoption of employee involvement practices between large and small firms. There are differences on two facilitators. Larger companies are

Table 13.2. Firm Size and Nature of EI Efforts.	
Firm Size Is Significantly, Positively Correlated with the Following:	
Stimulus for Employee Involvement	No differences
Reasons for Employee Involvement	Ethical/value reasons
Implementation Procedures	Philosophy/policy statement Procedure manual Written management objectives Formal measurement of EI activities Internal consultants External consultants
Spending on Employee Involvement	No differences
Barriers	No differences
Facilitators	Availability of resources Decentralization of decision-making authority

more likely to cite the availability of resources and the decentralization of decision-making authority as facilitators. These findings are consistent with the existence of greater slack in larger firms and with the need to overcome a tendency toward centralization of decision making.

Although there are differences in the level of adoption of employee involvement practices and the structuring of employee involvement efforts in large and small firms, these differences do not necessarily translate into differences in performance (see Table 13.3). There was no relationship between firm size and the impact of employee involvement practices on performance (productivity, quality, and so forth), and the only reward or power-sharing practice that was rated as having a greater impact on performance in larger firms was skill-based pay. This represents a change from the 1987 survey, in which larger firms reported greater impact of their employee involvement efforts on quality, profitability, customer service, and employee satisfaction.

As employee involvement practices have become more widely used and knowledge about installing them has become more widespread, perhaps the advantage enjoyed by larger firms has been disappearing. Moreover, as large organizations attempt to broaden coverage, the difficulty of achieving fundamental change in such a large, complex social system may become evident. Nevertheless, larger firms were still more likely to indicate improvements in three internal business conditions as a result of employee involvement: better union-management relations, moving decision-making authority lower in the organization, and better employee safety and health.

Overall, larger companies adopt employee involvement practices more broadly and formalize these practices more, but small firms enjoy almost as much success as large firms do in their employee involvement efforts. This finding may indicate that large firms need to do more in order to achieve the same level of success as smaller firms, given the disadvantages of organizational size.

Table 13.3. Firm Size and Effects of EI Efforts.

Firm Size Is Significantly Correlated with the Following:

Performance Impact	No differences
Changes in Internal Business Conditions	Union-management relations Moving decision-making authority lower Employee safety/health

Service Versus Manufacturing. Historically, manufacturing firms have been recognized as the leading adopters of employee involvement practices. Auto firms (Ford and General Motors) have made heavy use of union-management quality of work life programs; aerospace firms (Lockheed, Honeywell, Rockwell) have made heavy use of quality circles; food manufacturing firms (Procter & Gamble, General Foods, General Mills, Quaker Oats) and paper companies (Mead, Champion) have made heavy use of self-managing teams. Employee involvement approaches are becoming increasingly common in some segments of the service sector, notably telecommunications and insurance. In general, however, it is difficult to find many prominent examples of firms that have made heavy use of employee involvement practices in banking, hotels, restaurants, transportation, utilities, and other service businesses.

An interesting debate is emerging between proponents and opponents of employee involvement in service firms (Bowen and Lawler, 1992). Proponents (for example, Carlzon, 1987; Schlesinger and Heskett, 1991) argue that empowering service employees can lead to quicker response to customer needs, better employee morale, more friendly customer service, service innovations, and word-of-mouth customer advertising. Opponents (for example, Tansik, 1990) argue that empowerment entails costly selection and training practices, higher labor costs, slower and inconsistent service, and bad decision making.

Because our study covered the Fortune 500 manufacturing companies and the Fortune 500 service companies, we are in a good position to examine differences in the nature of employee involvement efforts in the two types of firms. Our total sample of 313 firms includes 167 (53 percent) from the manufacturing sector and 146 (47 percent) from the service sector. Since we examined service and manufacturing differences in our 1987 survey, we can also look at trends in the differences between service and manufacturing firms.

Manufacturing firms have adopted a wide range of employee involvement practices more aggressively than service firms (see Table 13.4). The only practices that service firms are more likely to adopt are the all-salaried work force and flexible benefits. Manufacturing firms are more likely to share information on units' operating results and competitors' performance; to provide training on decision making, team building, and especially quality and statistical analysis; to use skill-based pay and gainsharing; and to use quality circles, participation groups, union-management committees, minienterprise units, and self-managing teams.

The general pattern from 1987 to 1990 is that the differences between manufacturing and service companies are accelerating. In 1987, manufacturing firms were more likely to use only one information-sharing practice (unit operating results), rather than two, as in 1990; one training practice (quality skills), rather than three; no reward practices, rather

	Table 13.4. Service/Manufacturing Differences in EI Practices.	
Service Firms Use More		**Manufacturing Firms Use More**
	Information	
	Unit operating results	X
	Competitors' performance	X
	Knowledge	
	Decision making/problem solving	X
	Quality/statistical analysis	X
	Team building	X
	Rewards	
X	All-salaried work force	
X	Flexible benefits	
	Skill-based pay	X
	Gainsharing	X
	Power	
	Quality circles	X
	Participation groups	X
	Union-management QWL committees	X
	Minienterprise units	X
	Self-managing teams	X

than two; and four power-sharing practices (quality circles, participation groups, union-management committees, and self-managed teams), rather than five. Projections of future use of reward and power-sharing practices by manufacturing and service firms are consistent with this pattern. Manufacturing companies project relatively more future use of participation groups, union-management committees, self-managing teams, the all-salaried work force, skill-based pay, and gainsharing. Service companies expect relatively greater future adoptions only of individual incentives, an approach that is losing favor in the manufacturing sector. Manufacturers also project greater increases in spending on employee involvement than service firms do. (Section 20 presents more data on future use.)

Employee involvement efforts also appear to be implemented differently in service and manufacturing firms (Table 13.5). Employee involvement efforts in manufacturing firms are more likely to be stimulated by operating unit line managers, as well as by unions; the latter finding probably reflects, in part, the greater penetration of unions into the manufacturing sector. As in 1987, service firms were more likely to adopt employee involvement as a way of improving employee morale. By contrast with 1987, however, in 1990 service firms were not less interested in the performance advantages of employee involvement.

Manufacturing firms are more likely to use formal implementation procedures, including a philosophy or policy statement, written management objectives, internal consultants, and external consultants. For example, 73 percent of manufacturers, but only 53 percent of service firms, used internal consultants; and 70 percent of manufacturers, but only 53 percent of service firms, used external consultants. This is a major shift from 1987, when service firms were more likely to use formalized implementation procedures.

Table 13.5. Service/Manufacturing Differences in Nature of EI Efforts.

More True of Service Firms		More True of Manufacturing Firms
Stimulus for Employee Involvement		
	Operating unit line manager	X
	Unions	X
Reasons for Employee Involvement		
X	To improve employee morale	
Implementation Procedures		
	Philosophy/policy statement	X
	Written management objectives	X
	Internal consultants	X
	External consultants	X
Spending on Employee Involvement		
	Increases in future spending on employee involvement	X
Barriers		
	Short-term performance pressure	X
X	Centralization of decision making	
Facilitators		
	Employment security	X

In 1990, manufacturers were more likely to see short-term performance pressure as a barrier to employee involvement and were less likely to see centralization of decision making as a barrier. They also saw employment security as more of a facilitator. This finding may reflect the changing employment picture in the service sector, where previously stable companies (as in financial services) have recently undertaken major layoffs for the first time in many years.

Not only do manufacturers adopt more employee involvement practices and formalize them more than their service counterparts, they also experience far greater impact from their employee involvement efforts (see Table 13.6). This repeats the pattern from 1987, but the differences are even more dramatic. Manufacturers report a higher impact from their employee involvement efforts on seven of nine indicators: productivity, quality, worker satisfaction, turnover, absenteeism, competitiveness, and profitability. Manufacturers also report more impact on a variety of

Table 13.6. Service/Manufacturing Differences in Effects of EI Efforts.

More True of Service Firms	More True of Manufacturing Firms
Performance Impact	
Productivity	X
Quality of product/service	X
Worker satisfaction	X
Turnover	X
Absenteeism	X
Competitiveness	X
Profitability	X
Changes in Internal Business Conditions	
Improved implementation of technology	X
Elimination of management layers	X
More participative management style	X
Improved union-management relations	X
Moving decision-making authority lower	X
Broadened skill development	X
Increased information flow	X
Increased employee trust in management	X
Improved management decision making	X
Employee safety/health	X
Improved organizational processes/procedures	X

internal business conditions, including improved use of technology, elimination of management layers, more participative management style, better union-management relations, more lower-level decision making and skill, increased information flow, more employee trust in management, better management decision making, better safety and health, and better organizational processes and procedures.

The general pattern suggests that employee involvement is more of a marginal activity in service firms than in manufacturing firms. It is less likely to be initiated by line management, less likely to be rooted in formalized operating procedures, and simply less widely used. The result is that employee involvement efforts have less impact in service firms.

On the basis of our 1987 study, we predicted that there would be an increase in the use of employee involvement practices by service firms in the future, so that manufacturing and service firms would look more similar at some point (Lawler, Ledford, and Mohrman, 1989). This clearly has not happened. The question remains of whether service firms will make more use of employee involvement practices in the future.

We continue to expect that the use of employee involvement in service organizations will rise at some point during the 1990s, for several reasons. Service firms tend to be innovation laggards in a variety of areas, not just employee involvement. They tend to imitate practices that have been well established in the manufacturing sector. As employee involvement continues to be more widely accepted by U.S. managers generally, and as success stories from the manufacturing sector are more widely disseminated, we believe more service firms will experiment with employee involvement. Moreover, service firms have yet to experience the full force of the competitive forces that have led manufacturers to embrace employee involvement. Foreign competition, while not a factor in some segments of the service sector, is a growing threat to banking, financial services, airlines, and other important service businesses. Deregulation is an ongoing process in banking, financial services, insurance, and utilities. Dissatisfaction with poor productivity in the service sector appears to be growing. Such conditions encourage firms to look for new solutions, including employee involvement.

Type of Industry. We analyzed changes in the use of employee involvement practices in twelve different industries. An industry was included in this analysis if at least eight firms in it responded to both the 1987 and the 1990 surveys. The industry analysis covers five manufacturing industries (chemicals, electronics, food, forest products, and motor vehicles and parts) and seven service industries (diversified services, commercial banks, diversified financial services, savings institutions, life insurance companies, transportation, and utilities).

The number of service industries included in this analysis is higher than the number of manufacturing industries, and the number of companies is also higher, on average, in the service industries. This reflects the fact that the Fortune Service 500 are clustered into fewer industries, each with more companies, than are the Fortune Manufacturing 500.

Our comparisons are based on firms' employee involvement index scores. The index score may be thought of as representing the degree of coverage of the employee population, measured on a 7-point scale, for the average employee involvement practice. For example, an index score of 3.0 means that the company covered 21–40 percent of employees with the average employee involvement practice. (Resource C provides more information about the index scores.)

Table 13.7 displays the employee involvement index scores for 1987 and 1990 for the overall samples and for firms in twelve industries. A few general observations about the scores are warranted. The index scores indicate that the average EI practice covers only a minority of employees in Fortune 1000 firms. The index scores for the overall sample and for all industries are between 2.4 and 2.9 on the 7-point scale. This is between the point on the scale corresponding to the coverage of 1–20 percent of employees and the point corresponding to coverage of 21–40 percent of employees. Moreover, there was little change from 1987 to 1990 on the index scores. They inched upward, from 2.6 to 2.7.

Table 13.7. EI Index Scores by Industry.

	1987		1990	
	N	**Mean**	**N**	**Mean**
All Companies	323	2.6	313	2.7
Chemicals	15	2.6	15	2.9
Electronics	12	2.7	18	2.8
Food	22	2.5	9	2.4
Forest products	12	2.4	12	2.5
Motor vehicles and parts	10	2.6	8	2.8
Diversified services	32	2.8	26	2.5
Commercial banks	43	2.7	25	2.6
Diversified financial services	14	2.5	13	2.9
Savings institutions	15	2.4	10	2.5
Life insurance companies	21	2.8	19	2.7
Transportation	12	2.6	21	2.6
Utilities	21	2.7	26	2.5

The most surprising finding is that there is little variation in industry scores. Only one industry index score is greater than two-tenths of a point higher or lower than the grand mean in either year. The exception is food manufacturing in 1990, which is three-tenths of a point lower than the grand mean in 1990. Similarly, the differences in industry scores for the highest and lowest industries are small. In 1987, the industries with the lowest scores (forest products and savings institutions) are four-tenths of a point from the highest (diversified services and life insurance). The spread between highest and lowest in 1990 is half a point (food manufacturing versus chemicals and diversified financial services).

There also is little change within industries from 1987 to 1990. The largest changes are in diversified financial services (which experienced an increase from 2.5 to 2.9), chemicals (increasing from 2.6 to 2.9), and diversified services (decreasing from 2.8 to 2.5). No other changes in industry scores are large enough to represent practically or statistically significant changes.

The industries reporting the highest use of employee involvement practices in 1990 are chemicals, diversified financial services, electronics, and motor vehicles and parts. The industries reporting the lowest levels of use are food manufacturing, forest products, diversified services, savings institutions, and utilities. In general, these results correspond to reports of employee involvement in the popular and business press. The major exceptions to this pattern are food manufacturing and forest products. These industries scored low despite having some firms that are well-publicized users of employee involvement practices (for example, Procter & Gamble, General Mills, Mead, and Weyerhaeuser). This finding suggests either that the level of use of employee involvement practices by these firms is overstated or that these firms stand out as exceptions in their industries.

SECTION 14

Unionization and Employee Involvement

The role of unions in employee involvement efforts has been the subject of intense debate. The backdrop for this debate is the steady decline of union membership in American corporations. Only 12 percent of the private sector work force belongs to a union, versus one-third of the work force at the high-water mark just a few decades ago (Hoerr, 1991). The debate has engaged those within the labor movement (for example, AFL–CIO, 1985; Parker and Slaughter, 1988), as well as outside observers (for example, Heckscher, 1988; Hoerr, 1991). Some union supporters fear that employee involvement is just another way for management to manipulate workers and undermine unions, whereas others hope that joint union-management employee involvement efforts will bring benefits to union members, bring credit to union leaders, and help bring about more constructive union-management relationships.

The intensity of discussion about these issues has not impeded unions from engaging with company managements in the development of employee involvement efforts. Virtually every major national union has been involved in significant union-management employee involvement programs. The United Auto Workers, the United Steelworkers of America, and the Communications Workers of America have been particularly active in employee involvement projects. Therefore, the question is not whether unions can be engaged in employee involvement efforts but rather what forms these efforts take and what results they achieve.

Figure 14.1 examines the level of union involvement in employee involvement efforts in firms for which at least part of the work force is unionized. The results indicate that, in general, unions are only somewhat involved in these efforts. Unions are seen as greatly or very greatly involved in only 15 percent of companies with unions. The overall pattern of involvement has hardly changed from 1987 to 1990.

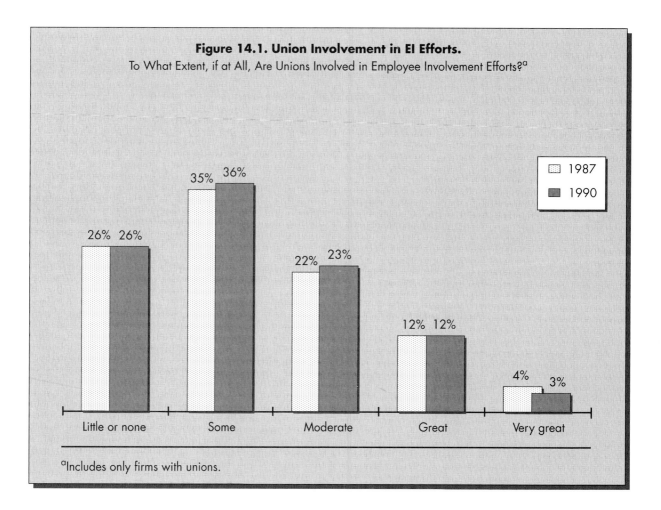

Figure 14.1. Union Involvement in EI Efforts.
To What Extent, if at All, Are Unions Involved in Employee Involvement Efforts?[a]

1987
1990

26% 26% — Little or none
35% 36% — Some
22% 23% — Moderate
12% 12% — Great
4% 3% — Very great

[a]Includes only firms with unions.

This pattern is disturbing for the union movement. It suggests that union leaders are not influencing employee involvement activities, which creates the potential for conflict between management and unions over employee involvement efforts. In the absence of union involvement, there are distinct limits to the scope of employee involvement activities. Pay systems, job classifications, work rules, and other important issues are collective bargaining matters, and these cannot be effectively addressed in the absence of union involvement. The danger is that employee involvement efforts may become trivialized because they cannot encompass important organizational issues. In addition, some have argued that employee involvement efforts that do not include unions are more likely to undermine unions than those in which union leaders play an active role (Herrick, 1990).

How does unionization affect the types of employee involvement practices that are used? Table 14.1 indicates the relationship between the percentage of the work force represented by a union and use of employee involvement practices. In general, there are few differences in the use of various information, knowledge, and power-sharing practices that are related to degree of unionization. Heavily unionized firms are more likely to share information about competitors' performance, less likely to offer training in how to understand the business, less likely to use survey feedback, and more likely to use union-management committees. Not surprisingly, the strongest correlation by far (.37) is between degree of unionization and use of union-management QWL committees.

Table 14.1. Unionization and EI Practices.

Degree of Unionization Is Significantly Correlated with Use of the Following Practices:

Information	More information on competitors' performance
Knowledge	Less training in understanding the business
Rewards	Less use of the following: All-salaried work force Profit sharing Individual incentives Work group/team incentives Employee stock ownership plans Flexible benefit plans
Power	Less use of survey feedback More use of union-management QWL committees

The major factor related to the degree of unionization is in the use of reward innovations. The more unionized the firm, the less likely it is to use an all-salaried work force, profit sharing, individual incentives, work-group or team incentives, ESOPs, and flexible benefits. This supports our comments about the consequences of lack of union involvement in the employee involvement effort. This general pattern is consistent with that found in 1987.

Unionization is also negatively related to the use of some human resource innovations, including hiring based on employee input, flextime, and cross-training. This is consistent with the perception of unionized workplaces as being somewhat less flexible than others.

As Table 14.2 indicates, degree of unionization has some effects on the way employee involvement programs are structured. In highly unionized settings, the stimulus for employee involvement is less likely to be operating unit line management, staff management, or the union. The latter finding once again indicates lack of leadership on the part of unions, in many cases; unions in heavily unionized firms are actually less likely than others to initiate employee involvement activities. There are no differences related to the reasons for implementing employee involvement.

Table 14.2. Unionization and Nature of EI Efforts.

Unionization Is Significantly Correlated
with the Following:

Stimulus for Employee Involvement	Less stimulus from: Operating unit line management Operating unit staff Unions
Reasons for Employee Involvement	No differences
Implementation Procedures	Greater use of internal EI facilitators, trainers, and consultants
Future Employee Involvement Efforts	Projected increase in future EI spending Future involvement of unions in EI efforts
Barriers	No differences
Facilitators	Greater availability of resources

Unionization is positively related to the use of internal employee involvement facilitators, trainers, and consultants. Indeed, in many companies, full-time positions of this kind are created for union members. There are no differences in barriers to employee involvement, and the only significant relationship between unionization and facilitators is the greater availability of resources associated with greater unionization. This probably reflects the positive relationship between organizational size and degree of unionization.

In general, level of unionization is not related to impact on performance of employee involvement efforts. There is a positive relationship only between unionization and impact of employee involvement on absenteeism. With respect to changes in internal business conditions, there is a positive relationship between level of unionization and degree to which employee involvement promotes better union-management relationships and employee safety and health, two long-term goals of the union movement. The more important finding may be that degree of unionization had no negative effects on any performance area or on any change in internal business conditions. Therefore, the belief of some managers that unions are a barrier to effective employee involvement efforts is not supported by our data.

An interesting pattern appears in the 1990 data. Level of unionization is related to current level of union involvement in employee involvement efforts, projected use of union-management QWL committees, and future increases in spending on employee involvement efforts. This represents a shift since 1987. Together, these relationships suggest a positive future for employee involvement in heavily unionized firms. This pattern may be an indication that management in unionized firms is becoming more willing to work with unions in developing employee involvement efforts.

Even more encouraging for those interested in cooperative union-management efforts is another pattern in the 1990 data. For firms in which at least some employees belong to a union, we asked about the degree of union involvement in the company's employee involvement efforts. Table 14.3 shows the relationship between degree of union involvement and effects of employee involvement efforts. Degree of union involvement was related to two performance outcomes: productivity and competitiveness. Even more impressive is that degree of union involvement is related to every internal business condition except elimination of management layers. Degree of union involvement was strongly related to improved implementation of new technology, change to a more participative management style, better union-management relations, greater decision making at lower levels of the organization, movement of performance-based rewards to lower levels, broadened skill development at lower levels, increased information flow, employee trust in management,

Table 14.3. Degree of Union Involvement and Effects of EI Efforts.

Degree of Union Involvement in EI Efforts Is Significantly, Positively Correlated with the Following:

Performance Impact	Productivity
	Competitiveness
	Improved implementation of technology
	More participative management style
	Better union-management relations
	Moving decision making lower
Changes in Internal Business Conditions	Moving performance-based rewards lower
	Broadened skill development
	Increased information flow
	Increased employee trust in management
	Improved management decision making
	Improved employee safety/health
	Improved processes/procedures

improved management decision making, improved employee safety and health, and improved organizational processes and procedures. This very consistent pattern supports our belief that in unionized firms it is difficult to develop effective employee involvement efforts that do not involve the union. Efforts that do not involve the union may become trivialized by the need to avoid collective bargaining matters. When the union is involved, however, they can lead to significant improvements.

SECTION 15

Competitive Conditions

The increased competition that many U.S. companies face has been well documented. One response is to adopt employee involvement practices in order to gain the advantages they offer. In the 1990 survey, we asked questions about the competitive conditions that companies face. In this section, we investigate the relationship between competitive market conditions and employee involvement.

Downsizing and Delayering. During the past decade, companies took many measures to strengthen their competitive positions. Results from our 1990 survey show that a very common approach was to reduce payroll costs and management overhead costs by downsizing and/or reducing layers of management. During the past decade, 74 percent of the Fortune

1000 companies reported that they had downsized, and 77 percent had reduced layers of management. Sixty-six percent had done both.

There has been considerable debate about whether a move toward employee involvement is possible in an environment characterized by downsizing and delayering. On the one hand, these activities may result in greater job insecurity and less loyalty to the company as individuals lose the sense that the company will take care of them as long as they do a good job. In addition, there are stories of the guilt felt by the survivors of a downsizing process and of work overload as fewer employees remain to do the work once done by many more. On the other hand, reduction in the numbers and layers of managers can result in more autonomy and responsibility for employees and fewer needed approvals. This change can produce swifter decision making and more ownership over the decisions that are made.

Table 15.1 shows the relationship of downsizing and reducing management levels to the adoption of employee involvement practices and to

| | Compared with Those That Have Not | |
	Firms That Have Downsized (N = 216)	Firms That Have Removed Layers (N = 229)
Table 15.1. Relationship of Downsizing and Removing Layers to Employee Involvement.		
Practices		
Gainsharing		more use
Skill-based pay		less use
Union-management QWL committees		more use
Minienterprise units		more use
Impact		
Participatory management style		greater impact
Improved union/management relations		greater impact
Moving decision making lower		greater impact
Broad skill development		greater impact
Improved processes and procedures		greater impact

their impact. Although there is a large overlap between the companies that downsize and those that remove layers, removing layers of management is more highly related both to adoption of employee involvement practices and to their impact on internal business conditions. Removal of management layers is often suggested as a desired benefit of employee involvement. When it occurs, it also facilitates and may even necessitate greater employee involvement by changing the architecture of the company in such a way that decisions and involvement must move down because there are not as many managers to decide and direct.

The greater use of gainsharing and minienterprise units by companies that are reducing layers suggests a management philosophy of linking

Employee Involvement Practices and Impact	Downsizing Prior to EI	Same Time	Downsizing After Mature EI
Table 15.2. Time of Downsizing: Comparison of Practices and Impact.			
Information			
Unit operating results			greater use
Competitors' performance			greater use
Knowledge			
Business understanding			greater use
Quality/statistical analysis		greater use	greater use
Team building			greater use
Job skills			greater use
Rewards			greater use
Cross-training			greater use
Rewards			
Profit sharing			greater use
Nonmonetary rewards			greater use
Power			
Survey feedback			greater use
Job enrichment			greater use
Quality circles			greater use
Impact			
Broader lower-level skills development			greater impact

employees closely to the measurable performance of their units. The use of skill-based pay reflects the greater importance of breadth of knowledge and development of self-management skills in organizations with fewer layers of management.

The impact pattern suggests that reducing layers is having its intended consequences. Firms that have reduced layers report that their employee involvement efforts have resulted in a more participatory management style, broad skills development, and the movement of decisions lower in the organization. Other benefits are improvement of processes and procedures and improved union-management relations.

In patterns of adopting employee involvement practices and in their impact, firms that have downsized are not much different overall from those that have not. The timing of downsizing with respect to the adoption of employee involvement does seem to matter, however. Companies that downsized prior to EI and companies that downsized and adopted EI simultaneously were no more or less likely to adopt employee involvement practices than other companies. However, companies that downsized after their employee involvement efforts had become somewhat mature have adopted more practices than those that downsized prior to or early in the life of their employee involvement programs. The results in Table 15.2 indicate that these companies invest extensively in sharing information and developing work-force skill. They also implement several reward- and power-oriented approaches more extensively than the others: job redesign, survey feedback, quality circles, profit sharing, and nonmonetary rewards. These approaches represent rather modest departures from the status quo. With the possible exception of profit sharing, they all leave intact the relative distribution of power and rewards in the organization.

Given the overall pattern of adoption, it is not surprising that the development of skills lower in the organization was the major area in which companies that downsized after employee involvement experienced greater impact from their employee involvement transitions. It is possible that these firms began their employee involvement programs at a time when they were not yet feeling major competitive pressures. They may have felt that they could afford the luxury of a human development–oriented program that focused on knowledge, information, and problem solving, and they may not yet have felt pressure for significant deviation from the status quo in other areas.

Market Conditions. We also asked companies about the kinds of competitive market conditions they were facing. At least two-thirds of the companies were experiencing the following market conditions to some extent: foreign competition, shorter product life cycles, declining markets, and rapid growth.

Table 15.3 shows that growth or decline in markets appears to make very little difference in the adoption of employee involvement, probably because decline in markets makes it difficult to justify transition costs, and growing markets mask the need for increased involvement.

Two conditions that are strongly related to the adoption of employee involvement practices are foreign competition and shorter product life cycles. These two market conditions are apparently quite conducive to

Employee Involvement Practices	Foreign Competition	Shorter Product Life Cycles	Declining Markets	Growing Markets
Information				
Overall operating results	*			
Unit operating results	**			
Competitors' performance	***			
Knowledge				
Group problem solving	***	**		*
Leadership	*	***		**
Business understanding		**		
Quality/statistical analysis	***	***	*	
Team building	***	***		*
Cross-training		*		
Rewards				
All-salaried work force		*		**
Skill-based pay	***			
Profit sharing		**		
Gainsharing	*			
Individual incentives		*	*	
Stock ownership		*		
Power				
Job redesign	***	***		
Quality circles	***	**		
Participation groups	***	*		
Union-management QWL committees	***			
Minienterprises	**	*	*	
Self-managing teams	***	**		

Correlation: * = weak but significant ($p \leq .05$)

     ** = moderate relationship ($p \leq .01$)

     *** = strong relationship ($p \leq .001$)

Table 15.3. Relationship of Market Conditions to Adoption of EI Practices.

employee involvement. Companies with a greater amount of foreign competition share three kinds of key competitive information more broadly: overall results, unit operating results, and competitors' performance. These companies also invest in more training. Most important, they have adopted nontraditional distributions of power and reward. Gainsharing and skill-based pay both alter the traditional logic of organizational rewards. Except for survey feedback, every power approach is more widely used by companies with more foreign competition.

The impact of shorter product life cycles is also significant. Companies that feel more pressure in this area are more likely to invest in training and development, slightly more likely to use rewards, and very much more likely to adopt various power-sharing approaches.

Increasing competition and shorter product life cycles present very specific business conditions that have to be addressed. Companies experiencing these to a greater extent apparently decide that they can address them best by getting their employees involved in meeting the challenge. Table 15.4 indicates that these companies feel that their employee involvement programs are paying off in some very significant ways. They

Performance Indicators	Foreign Competition	Shorter Product Life Cycles	Declining Markets	Growing Markets
Productivity	***	*		
Quality of products or services	**	*		
Customer service		**		
Worker satisfaction	***			
Competitiveness	*	*		
Profitability	**	*	*	
Employee quality of work life			***	

Table 15.4. Relationship of Market Conditions to Impact of Employee Involvement on Performance.

Correlation: * = weak but significant ($p \leq .05$)
** = moderate relationship ($p \leq .01$)
*** = strong relationship ($p \leq .001$)

Table 15.5. Relationship of Market Conditions to Impact of Employee Involvement on Internal Business Conditions.

Internal Business Condition	Foreign Competition	Shorter Product Life Cycles	Declining Markets	Growing Markets
Improved implementation of technology	*			
Eliminated layers of management or supervision	***	**		
Changed management style to one that is more participatory	***	*		
Improved union-management relations	***			
Moved decision-making authority to lower organizational level	***	**		
Moved performance-based rewards to lower organizational levels	**	**		**
Broadened skill development at lower organizational levels	***	***		
Increased information flow throughout the corporation	***	***		
Increased employee trust in management	**	**		
Improved management decision making	***	***		
Improved employee safety/health	***			
Improved organizational processes and procedures	*			**

Correlation: * = weak but significant ($p \leq .05$)
   ** = moderate relationship ($p \leq .01$)
   *** = strong relationship ($p \leq .001$)

are more likely to feel that increased productivity, quality, competitiveness, and profitability are outcomes. This finding contrasts with the impact in declining markets, where employee involvement is related only to increases in profitability and employees' quality of work life. The extent to which a company is dealing with rapidly growing markets is not related to any performance outcomes.

Table 15.5 repeats this pattern. The extent of foreign competition is strongly related to changes in every internal business condition that we asked about. The impact of shorter product life cycles is less consistent but still impressively linked to these outcomes. Apparently, these companies not only implement many practices but also do so in a way that achieves the desired changes in functioning and performance. With two exceptions, growth and decline do not differentiate the impact of employee involvement in these areas. The exception is that companies with growing markets are more likely to report that employee involvement resulted in moving performance-based rewards lower in the organization, and improved processes and procedures.

The competitive environment does seem to make a difference, both in the adoption of employee involvement practices and in the results they achieve. Companies that respond by reducing management layers, for example, are more likely to have adopted practices that significantly alter the distribution of power and rewards in the organization than are those that simply downsize. Companies that had established a relatively mature employee involvement program before downsizing are more likely to have distributed information and knowledge throughout the organization. Foreign competition and shorter product life cycles are related to more use of employee involvement approaches and to greater change in performance and in internal business conditions. These very specific challenges appear to catalyze a great deal of effective effort to make the transition. The extent of growth and decline in markets is generally not related to the extent of use or to the effectiveness of employee involvement practices.

PART FIVE

Total Quality Management Programs

SECTION 16

Adoption of Total Quality Programs and Practices

The management literature during the last half of the 1980s saw a tremendous increase in the attention paid to quality and total quality management programs (see, for example Deming, 1986; Juran, 1989). The United States government established the Malcolm Baldrige National Quality Award, which is given annually to companies that have outstanding total quality programs. One U.S. company, Florida Power and Light, even received the prestigious Deming award for its total quality management program; previously, it had been given only to Japanese organizations. In many respects, total quality management programs and employee involvement programs are intertwined. In Section 18, we will look at this interface more closely. The focus here is on the rate of adoption of total quality programs and practices.

Seventy-seven percent of the companies responding to our 1990 survey said that some of their employees were covered by total quality programs. On the average, 41 percent of employees in companies with total quality programs are covered by them. A surprisingly large 17 percent of the companies surveyed reported that they covered 100 percent of their employees with total quality programs of some kind. These companies clearly are trying to make total quality a way of life. Overall, it is obvious that quality programs have had an impact on most organizations.

In Section 5, data were presented on the use of quality circles and problem-solving groups, both of which are frequently part of total quality management programs in companies. Table 16.1 shows how frequently seven specific total quality management practices, which might be part of an overall TQM program, are adopted. The pattern for all but two of these is very similar. Most organizations use direct employee exposure to customers, self-inspection, work simplification, cost-of-quality monitoring, and collaboration with suppliers on quality efforts. In the typical organization, however, these affect less than 40 percent of employees. This finding fits with the earlier point that most total quality programs do not affect all employees in an organization. One contributor to this situation may well be the fact that many quality programs start in manufacturing areas and at lower levels of organizations; as a result, the biggest impact is on the production floor. In service organizations, a parallel pattern often develops. Total quality starts as a

Table 16.1. Percentage of Employees Covered by Total Quality Practices.

	None 0%	Almost None 1–20%	Some 21–40%	About Half 41–60%	Most 61–80%	Almost All 81–99%	All 100%
Direct employee exposure to customers	4	32	31	16	4	4	0
Self-inspection	10	25	31	14	7	7	0
Work simplification	13	26	33	12	7	7	0
Cost-of-quality monitoring	18	35	24	11	4	4	3
Collaboration with suppliers in quality efforts	13	37	27	11	3	3	2
Just-in-time deliveries	24	31	22	11	4	4	2
Work cells or manufacturing cells	41	27	19	9	2	2	0

customer service-oriented activity, which largely affects those individuals who directly serve customers.

Two total quality practices—just-in-time deliveries, and work cells or manufacturing cells —are much less frequently adopted and typically cover a lower percentage of the work force. This finding undoubtedly reflects the fact that these practices are particularly appropriate to manufacturing environments and the fact that both require major changes before they can be implemented. In the case of work cells, pieces of equipment must often be moved around, and a number of work flows must be changed. Similarly, just-in-time deliveries require significant adjustments in equipment, work methods, inventory procedures, and a host of other organizational practices.

The results show that total quality programs are in use in the vast majority of U.S. organizations and suggest that a fairly standard pattern of practices is typical of total quality programs. Like employee involvement programs, total quality in most organizations is still implemented in part of an organization and does not represent a total organizational commitment. This may change in the future, of course, as organizations become more sophisticated in managing total quality programs and as it becomes more apparent how to apply total quality programs to white-collar work and managerial work. For the moment, however, total quality practices are still used only in parts of the typical organization.

*Organizations
That Implement
Total Quality*

Earlier, we suggested that the use of various total quality practices reflects, in part, the fact that the early application of total quality programs was largely in manufacturing settings. This section explores in greater depth the kinds of firms using total quality approaches.

The information in Table 17.1 supports our belief that there has been more total quality effort in manufacturing settings. The percentage of a firm's operations in manufacturing is strongly positively correlated with the percentage of the firm's employees covered by total quality management and with the extent of use of each total quality practice. Work simplification is weakly positively correlated and direct exposure to customers is strongly negatively correlated with percentage of operations in manufacturing. Service firms are much more likely to employ direct

Table 17.1. Relationship Between Firm Characteristics and Adoption of Total Quality Practices.[a]

	Size (Number of Employees)	Percentage Manufacturing	Percentage Union
Percentage of Employees Covered by TQM	***	***	* (–)
Total Quality Practices			
Direct exposure to customers	*	*** (–)	
Self-inspection	*	***	* (–)
Work simplification	*	*	* (–)
Cost of quality monitoring		***	
Collaboration with suppliers in quality efforts		***	
Just-in-time deliveries	**	***	
Work cells or manufacturing cells	**	***	* (–)

Part Correlation: * = weak but significant ($p \leq .05$)
  ** = moderate relationship ($p \leq .01$)
  *** = strong relationship ($p \leq .001$)
(–) indicates a negative relationship.

[a]Relationship of each firm characteristic to quality practices is measured controlling for the other two characteristics (e.g., the relationship of size controls for its correlation to % manufacturing and % union).

exposure of employees to customers, probably because customer interface is often built into the nature of the service provided. The overall pattern of use of these quality approaches is similar to the pattern reported in Section 13, which showed much greater use of employee involvement practices among manufacturing firms than among service firms.

When controlling for size and percentage of manufacturing operations, unionization appears to have a small, negative impact on use of total quality practices. Self-inspection, work simplification, and the use of work cells are somewhat less likely to be used in unionized settings, and a smaller percentage of employees tend to be involved. Again, this builds on the finding in Section 14 that unionization is not strongly related to use of employee involvement practices, with the exception of a positive relationship to union-management QWL committees and a negative relationship to reward system changes.

Table 17.2. Relationship Between Market Conditions and Adoption of Total Quality Practices.

	Foreign Competition	Shorter Product Life Cycles	Declining Markets	Growing Markets
Percentage of Employees Covered by TQM	***	***	*	
Total Quality Practices				
Direct exposure to customers	*** (–)			*
Self-inspection	***	***		
Work simplification	*	*		*
Cost of quality monitoring	***	*		
Collaboration with suppliers in quality efforts	***	***		
Just-in-time deliveries	***	**		
Work cells or manufacturing cells	***	***	*	

Correlation: * = weak but significant ($p \leq .05$)

     ** = moderate relationship ($p \leq .01$)

       *** = strong relationship ($p \leq .001$)

(–) indicates a negative relationship.

The size of the firm makes a difference in adoption of total quality management, just as it does in adoption of employee involvement practices. Larger firms are likely to cover a larger percentage of the work force with total quality practices and are more likely to use each practice except cost-of-quality monitoring and collaboration with suppliers.

Competitive conditions also have a bearing on adoption of TQM, as they do on employee involvement (see Table 17.2). Again, companies facing foreign competition and shorter product life cycles cover more employees with their total quality programs and use every practice, except direct exposure to customers, with a greater percentage of their employees. Firms with greater foreign competition are actually less likely to have broad employee exposure to customers, reflecting the fact that firms with a greater manufacturing component are more likely to be experiencing intense foreign competition.

Repeating the employee involvement pattern, growth or decline of markets is not highly related to the use of total quality practices (see Table 17.3). To the extent that firms are in declining markets, they are somewhat more likely to involve more employees in their quality programs and to use work cells. These firms also tend to have larger manufacturing components. Firms in growing markets tend to have smaller

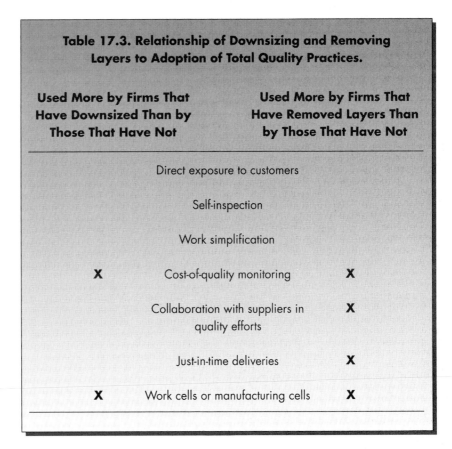

Table 17.3. Relationship of Downsizing and Removing Layers to Adoption of Total Quality Practices.

Used More by Firms That Have Downsized Than by Those That Have Not		Used More by Firms That Have Removed Layers Than by Those That Have Not
	Direct exposure to customers	
	Self-inspection	
	Work simplification	
X	Cost-of-quality monitoring	X
	Collaboration with suppliers in quality efforts	X
	Just-in-time deliveries	X
X	Work cells or manufacturing cells	X

manufacturing components and are more likely to expose their employees to customers and use work simplification.

Finally, we examined patterns of use of total quality practices among firms that have downsized, in comparison with those that have not (see Table 17.3). Downsizing is significantly associated with greater use of cost-of-quality monitoring and of work cells. Reducing layers of management is associated with both of these as well as more collaboration with suppliers in their quality efforts, and more use of just-in-time deliveries. Like employee involvement, reduction of layers is associated with fuller use of quality approaches, by comparison with firms that have not reduced layers. Similarity in patterns of who adopts employee involvement and who adopts total quality underscores the relatedness of these two phenomena in the United States at this time. It is also testimony to considerable overlap in philosophies and approaches.

Table 17.4 shows the results for an index of use of the seven total quality management practices. Firms in chemicals, electronics, and motor vehicles and parts were the manufacturing firms ranked highest in use of quality practices, just as they were the highest in the use of employee involvement practices. Firms in foods and forest products were lower in both. Among service firms, use patterns for total quality practices are not similar to use patterns for employee involvement practices. Total quality is not used to a substantial extent in any of the service indus-

Table 17.4. Total Quality Management Index Scores by Industry.

	Total Quality Index Mean
All Companies	2.8
Chemicals	3.2
Electronics	3.3
Food	2.5
Forest products	2.4
Motor vehicles and parts	3.1
Diversified services	2.8
Commercial banks	2.2
Diversified financial services	2.2
Savings institutions	2.3
Life insurance companies	2.2
Transportation	2.5
Utilities	2.5

tries. Its highest use, in diversified services, is still relatively low by comparison with the use level of leading manufacturing firms. Apparently, total quality management is in a very early stage of use in most service organizations.

SECTION 18

Relationships Between Employee Involvement and Total Quality

There is a great deal of conceptual overlap, but there are also some key differences, between organizational practices that are part of total quality and those that are part of employee involvement. Total quality management programs often establish quality circles and other participative groups, sometimes called quality-improvement teams, that are clearly a way of creating involvement and sharing power. Quality-improvement teams may take the place of quality circles, or they may complement the work of quality circles. They utilize problem-solving and process-control tools that overlap considerably with those utilized by quality circles. The teaching of these tools to employees throughout the organization constitutes a form of knowledge and skill development that expands the capacity of the work force to contribute and to manage their own work processes. Total quality's use of self-inspection and work cells can best be sustained by an explicit move toward self-management. In some settings, this may entail the establishment of self-managing teams.

A key contribution of the total quality movement has been its emphasis on the processes that cut across the organization, beginning with contact with customers and going all the way back to the interface with suppliers. This emphasis has been embodied in such practices as exposing employees directly to customers and collaborating with suppliers' quality efforts to ensure high-quality materials and enable just-in-time deliveries. These approaches are fully consistent with employee involvement, particularly when they are carried out by the line work units rather than by special staff groups and managers.

The employee involvement literature has focused more than the total quality literature has on aligning the motivational system in the organization through the creation of motivating jobs and the use of review and reward systems that emphasize performance. At face value, the emphasis of total quality on work simplification may seem to work at cross purposes with job enrichment. In fact, however, most total quality programs have not systematically addressed the issue of how jobs should be designed. It is possible that work process simplification can occur simultaneously with the creation of jobs that have the motivating characteristics of being "whole" and significant jobs, entailing autonomy and feedback (Hackman and Oldham, 1980). This is particularly likely to be true if it leads to reducing unnecessary steps and procedures while giving teams or individuals more responsibility for producing a whole product or service. It may also have the opposite impact, however, if it leads to excessive division of labor.

One arena in which the two literatures appear to be at odds concerns performance appraisal and rewards. The total quality literature has in some cases (Deming, 1986) cautioned against "management by fear" and especially against the establishment of individual appraisal systems and standards of performance. The argument is that these fail to take account of the reality that performance levels are more the product of characteristics of the system than of individual motivation and performance. As a result, practices that manage the performance of individuals have not been a central focus of implementation in total quality management.

Total quality's emphasis on the development of good process measures is fully consistent with employee involvement's emphasis on feedback but stops short of dealing with the relationship between work process management and team and individual performance management. It is assumed that the latter will follow from the former. Moreover, although the implication could be that teams rather than individuals should be managed, total quality efforts generally have not led to team-based performance management.

Table 18.1. Use of Quality Practices by Organizations with Different EI Use Patterns.

Quality Practices	Employee Involvement Patterns			
	Low Users	Average Users	High Users	Reward-Oriented Users
Direct exposure to customers	low	low	high	high
Self-inspection	low	low	high	high
Work simplification	low	average	average	high
Cost-of-quality monitoring	low	average	average	high
Collaboration with suppliers in quality efforts	low	average	average	high
Just-in-time deliveries	low	average	average	high
Work cell or manufacturing cells	low	average	average	high

One might also ask whether there are any philosophical incongruities between total quality management and employee involvement. The answer is that there are. For example, implementation of total quality tends to be more top-down in nature than is implementation of employee involvement. The management role that is advocated is more directive than that advocated in employee involvement. In addition, the utilization of problem-solving tools and such techniques as just-in-time deliveries may introduce a certain rigidity that can be interpreted as reducing employee control and discretion (see, for example, Klein, 1989, 1991).

Table 18.1 illustrates the prevalence in use of the various total quality management practices in our groupings of organizations according to their use of employee involvement practices. It can be seen that, in general, organizations with a greater commitment to employee involvement also have a greater commitment to total quality. High users of employee involvement tend to utilize direct employee exposure to customers and self-inspection more than others do.

Most interesting is that organizations with a rewards orientation to employee involvement tend to utilize total quality practices more than any of the other groupings. Given the relative lack of attention to rewards in writings on quality, this is a surprise. Nevertheless, the improvement orientation of total quality is quite compatible with the orientation of many involvement-related reward systems. For example, problem-solving and process-improvement groups are often advocated as mechanisms for effecting gains in gainsharing and team incentive programs.

We wanted to know how employee involvement and total quality management are related in companies that have used them both. Figure 18.1 illustrates these relationships. In more than half the cases (54 percent), employee involvement started first; 19 percent of the companies started both simultaneously. This pattern probably reflects the fact that employee involvement was popularized earlier in the United States. Early employee involvement, often entailing the establishment of quality circles and other participation groups, can set the stage for the systematization of these efforts through a total quality program. Total quality has also helped focus involvement efforts explicitly on the work of the firm and on measurements of its processes, thus enhancing their relevance to the competitive conditions that organizations face.

How the relationship between the two programs is managed can be a critical organizational choice. Having two approaches with different names may set the stage for competing programs in an organization. Figure 18.1 shows that the Fortune 1000 are split on the issue, with slightly more than one-third managing employee involvement and total quality as one integrated program, about one-third managing them

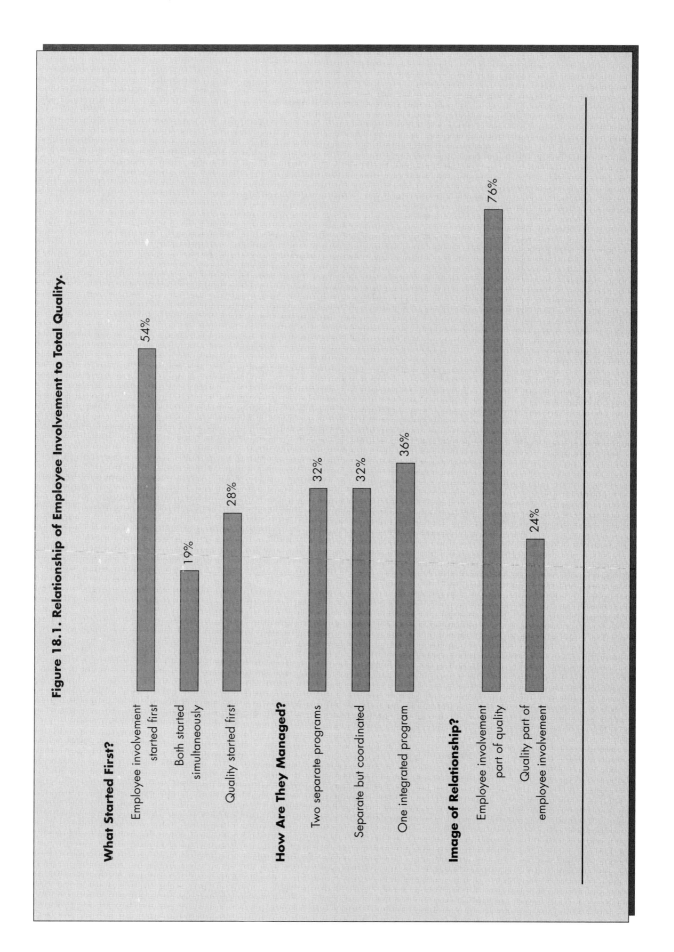

Figure 18.1. Relationship of Employee Involvement to Total Quality.

as separate but coordinated programs, and the other third managing them separately.

We also asked how the majority of managers viewed the relationship between employee involvement and total quality, and which effort tended to predominate. In three-quarters of the companies, the majority of managers see employee involvement as part of quality. This finding provides further evidence for the hypothesis that the focus of total quality is seen as more relevant to today's competitive business conditions. It may also be an easier concept to rally managers around, since on the surface it emphasizes work processes rather than issues of power and management style. Employee involvement, however, may be viewed as creating the organizational context needed to support quality-improvement processes.

SECTION 19

The Impact of Total Quality Management Programs

The impact of total quality management on various outcomes was not directly investigated. Given the substantial overlap between total quality and employee involvement, however, it is justifiable to ask whether more extensive users of total quality methodology are more likely to report that their employee involvement activities are producing positive results.

Because of different patterns in the use of both total quality and employee involvement by service and manufacturing companies, we report these results separately for companies that are primarily service and those that are primarily manufacturing. For the manufacturing firms, Table 19.1 relates the extent of coverage of employees with total quality and the extent of use of various total quality approaches to the reported impact of employee involvement on business performance and quality of work life outcomes. Table 19.2 reports the same results for service firms.

In manufacturing firms, the percentage of employees covered by total quality is related to two business performance outcomes: quality and customer service. In service firms, the extent of coverage of employees is related to productivity, quality, and competitiveness.

The extent of use of specific quality practices is related to performance. In manufacturing firms, the use of every total quality management practice is related to quality of products and services. Three of the practices are related to productivity: self-inspection, work simplification, and the use of work cells. None of the practices is related to competitiveness or profitability. Apparently, the use of quality approaches is related to operating indicators but not to financial and market results. Furthermore,

Table 19.1. Relationship of Use of Total Quality Practices to EI Impact in Manufacturing Firms.

	Productivity	Quality	Customer Service	Competitiveness	Profitability	Worker Satisfaction	Turnover	Absenteeism	QWL
Percentage of Employees Covered by TQM		*	*						
Total Quality Practices									
Direct exposure to customers		*	*						
Self-inspection	***	***	**						
Work simplification	*	***	***						
Cost-of-quality monitoring		***	**						
Collaboration with suppliers in quality efforts		**	**						
Just-in-time deliveries		**	**						
Work cells or manufacturing cells	*	***	***			*			
Overall index of quality practices	*	***	***						

Correlation: * = weak but significant ($p \leq .05$)
** = moderate relationship ($p \leq .01$)
*** = strong relationship ($p \leq .001$)

Table 19.2. Relationship of Use of Total Quality Practices to EI Impact in Service Firms.

	Productivity	Quality	Customer Service	Competitiveness	Profitability	Worker Satisfaction	Turnover	Absenteeism	QWL
Percentage of Employees Covered by TQM	***	**		*					
Total Quality Practices									
Direct exposure to customers		**	**	*					
Self-inspection			*	*	*				
Work simplification				*	*			*	*
Cost-of-quality monitoring					*				
Collaboration with suppliers in quality efforts			*				*	*	**
Just-in-time deliveries				*	**		*	***	
Work cells or manufacturing cells						*			
Overall index of quality practices			*	*	**	*	**	**	*

Correlation: * = weak but significant ($p \le .05$)
                 ** = moderate relationship ($p \le .01$)
                 *** = strong relationship ($p \le .001$)

with one exception, quality practices are not related to satisfaction, turn-over, absenteeism, or QWL. The exception is a weak, but significant, correlation between the use of work cells and worker satisfaction.

The picture in service firms is much different. One practice—direct exposure of employees to customers—is related to quality, customer service, and competitiveness. A number of quality practices, including self-inspection, work simplification, and work cells, are related to both competitiveness and profitability. In addition, the use of various practices is related to reductions in turnover and absenteeism. In particular, self-inspection, collaboration with suppliers, and just-in-time deliveries have positive effects. These relationships are somewhat surprising because they were not present in manufacturing firms.

The same pattern of relationships is evident when uses of all quality practices are combined in an overall index. In manufacturing firms, the use of total quality management is related only to the productivity, quality, and customer service outcomes of employee involvement. In service firms, total quality management is related to a different set of outcomes: competitiveness, profitability, and all the quality of work life outcomes. Customer service is the only outcome related to the overall extent of use of total quality management in both manufacturing and service companies.

The differences between service and manufacturing firms are striking. Manufacturing firms are heavier users of most employee involvement practices (see Table 13.4), and of all total quality practices, than service firms are. Overall, manufacturing companies report a greater impact from employee involvement than service firms do, but their use of total quality is related only to a subset of outcomes: productivity, quality, and customer service.

This difference in patterns may be partly a result of the greater length of time during which manufacturing firms have been employing these practices. Quality practices may have become part of the required "basics" of manufacturing firms and may no longer be a competitive advantage. In addition, the manufacturing function may not predominate in determining competitiveness and productivity. Market and economic forces, such as international financial and labor markets, may have a far greater impact on these outcomes. In service firms, by contrast, the use of total quality management is still relatively new and may represent a competitive advantage at this time. In addition, these firms are less likely to be subject to foreign competition and may be able to affect profitability and competitiveness more directly through the quality of the services they offer.

In manufacturing, the lack of impact of quality practices on such quality of work life indicators as satisfaction also contrasts with total quality impact on service firms. This may reflect the different reasons service and manufacturing firms embark on employee involvement. Service firms are more likely to be motivated by the desire to improve employee morale (see Table 13.5) and thus may implement both employee involvement and total quality in a way that focuses more directly on this issue.

This emphasis on quality of work life issues is critical to performance in service firms, where the essence of a service may be in the interface between employees and customers. There is good evidence that poor employee morale is apparent to customers (Bowen, 1986) and directly reduces the value of services. In addition, improvement in the quality of services provided can be expected to enhance employee morale, since employees are directly exposed to the anger and frustration of customers who are subjected to errors and poor service. Consequently, it is not surprising that providing employees with tools to improve the quality of services and empowering them to use the tools enhances both company performance and employee satisfaction.

A different picture emerges when we examine the relationship of the use of total quality management to the attainment of internal business conditions (see Table 19.3). Here, the extent of use of total quality practices in manufacturing and service firms alike is related to a wide range of employee involvement impacts. Use of quality practices is strongly related to the movement of decisions down the organization and to the improvement of management decision making in both service and manufacturing firms. In manufacturing firms, the use of quality practices is more strongly related to the elimination of layers of management, to the development of a participative style of management, to broad skill development, and to the improvement of processes and procedures. Again, this may reflect the fact that manufacturing firms have had quality practices in use longer than service firms have.

The complete lack of relationship in manufacturing between the adoption of total quality and the quality of work life of employees (shown in Table 19.1) seems incompatible with the finding that use of quality practices is related to a wide range of changes in internal business conditions. This pattern may reflect the tendency for manufacturing firms to focus on the technical aspects of quality improvement and less on the employee involvement–related aspects.

In service organizations, direct exposure of employees to customers is not related to altered organizational conditions, and this finding supports the notion that such exposure, rather than representing a change in philosophy and practice, as it does in manufacturing firms, is inherent in the jobs of employees of service organizations. Work cells also show little relationship to business conditions in service organizations, which no doubt reflects their infrequent use and the fact that this approach is relatively new to service organizations.

Table 19.3. Relationship of Use of Total Quality Practices to EI Impact on Internal Business Conditions.[a]

Internal Business Conditions	Percentage of Employees Covered by TQM	Direct Exposure to Customers	Self-Inspection	Work Simplification	Cost-of-Quality Monitoring	Collaboration with Suppliers	Just-in-Time Deliveries	Work or Manufacturing Cells
Improved implementation of technology	m = * s = **	m = ***	m = ***	m = *** s = ***	m = *** s = **	m = * s = **	m = **	m = ***
Eliminated layers of management or supervision	m = **	m = ***	m = **	m = ***	m = ***	m = *** s = **	m = *** s = ***	m = ***
Changed management style to one that is more participatory	m = *** s = *	m = ***	m = ***	m = ***	m = *** s = **	m = ***	m = ***	m = ***
Improved union-management relations	s = *	m = **		m = *	s = ***			
Moved decision-making authority to lower organizational level	m = ** s = **	m = *	m = *** s = *	m = ***	m = *** s = ***	m = *** s = ***	m = * s = ***	m = *** s = **
Moved performance-based rewards to lower organizational levels			m = *** s = **	m = ***	m = *** s = ***	m = **	s = *	
Broadened skill development at lower organizational levels	m = ** s = **	m = *	m = ***	m = ***	m = *** s = **	m = **	m = ** s = ***	m = **
Increased information flow throughout the corporation	m = * s = **	m = ***	m = **	m = *** s = *	m = ** s = **	m = * s = ***	m = **	m = ***
Increased employee trust in management			m = ** s = *	m = ** s = **	m = ** s = **	m = **	s = *	m = **
Improved management decision making	m = * s = **	m = **	m = *** s = *	m = *** s = **	m = *** s = **	m = *** s = **	m = ** s = **	m = ***
Improved employee safety/health			m = ** s = *	m = ** s = *	m = * s = *		s = **	m = ** s = *
Improved organizational processes and procedures	m = *** s = **	m = **	m = ***	m = ** s = **	m = *** s = **	m = ***	s = **	m = ***

Correlation: * = weak but significant ($p \leq .05$) ** = moderate relationship ($p \leq .01$) *** = strong relationship ($p \leq .001$)

[a] m = manufacturing firms (N = 148); s = service firms (N = 110)

We examined both the relationship between how quality and employee involvement are implemented and managed relative to one another and what success they achieve. There is no significant difference in the results of employee involvement programs between companies that see employee involvement as part of quality and those that see quality as part of employee involvement. Furthermore, different results are not reported by companies that started employee involvement first, second, or simultaneously with quality. These findings again substantiate the basic compatibility of the two approaches; either one can provide an equally effective first effort and can pave the way for the other. We do not have data on whether each is equally likely to lead to the other or whether companies that start with total quality programs may be more or less likely to adopt employee involvement practices.

What does make a major difference is the way the two programs are managed (see Table 19.4). If employee involvement and quality are managed as one integrated program or as two coordinated programs, they are more likely to achieve desired performance results and to change internal business conditions than if they are run as two separate programs. The three performance areas in which coordination and integration have the most positive effect are all critical aspects of business performance: quality, customer service, and competitiveness.

Running the programs separately reduces the impact on the transition to a high-involvement culture. Companies that run them separately are less likely to achieve a participatory management style, move decisions lower, and achieve broad skill development and information flow. They are also less likely to remove layers of management, which was found earlier to be associated with fuller implementation of both quality and employee involvement. Finally, they report less improvement in their technology implementation capabilities and in organizational processes and procedures.

In short, it appears that having two separate organizational initiatives, quality and employee involvement, strongly reduces their impact. Companies that take this approach do not attain as complete an implementation of either one and are not as likely to attain their desired outcomes. This is a very important finding, in view of the number of companies that have two different initiatives and two different support staffs vying for attention. It is very possible that such separation precludes recognition within the organization of the fundamental conceptual and action overlap and leaves organizational members confused and/or cynical about the change strategy. In fact, the two initiatives may be implemented incompatibly.

The implementation of quality practices appears to be very synergistic with the implementation of employee involvement. Companies with a greater degree of use of these tools are more likely to report positive outcomes from employee involvement in business performance and changes in internal operating conditions. Service companies are also more likely to experience enhanced quality of work life outcomes. Companies that integrate or coordinate the two initiatives experience considerably more positive change than do those that run separate total quality and employee involvement programs.

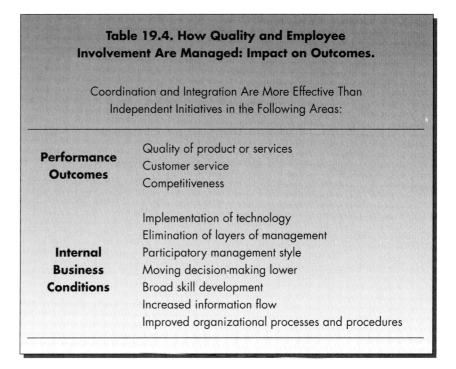

Table 19.4. How Quality and Employee Involvement Are Managed: Impact on Outcomes.

Coordination and Integration Are More Effective Than Independent Initiatives in the Following Areas:

Performance Outcomes	Quality of product or services Customer service Competitiveness
Internal Business Conditions	Implementation of technology Elimination of layers of management Participatory management style Moving decision-making lower Broad skill development Increased information flow Improved organizational processes and procedures

PART SIX

Employee Involvement
in the Future

SECTION 20

Plans for Adopting Employee Involvement Practices

Three questions in the survey addressed the future utilization of employee involvement practices. The first asked whether employee involvement is compatible with the types of changes organizations face. As discussed in Section 1, most organizations see EI as compatible with their needs to meet changes in technology, in the competitive environment, and in the work force. It is also seen as compatible with the pressure for improved performance and with current business strategy. This argues that increasing adoption of employee involvement activities is very likely.

Figure 20.1 offers data confirming the point that employee involvement spending is likely to be on the upswing. Most organizations report that

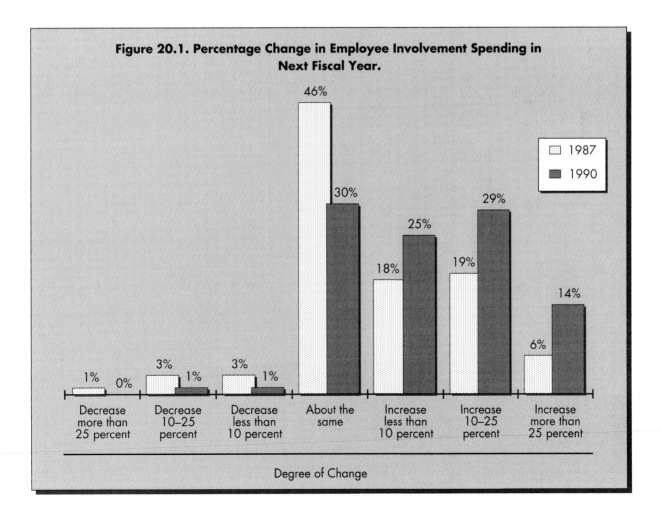

Figure 20.1. Percentage Change in Employee Involvement Spending in Next Fiscal Year.

1987
1990

46%
30%
25%
29%
18%
19%
14%
6%
1%
0%
3%
1%
3%
1%

Decrease more than 25 percent
Decrease 10–25 percent
Decrease less than 10 percent
About the same
Increase less than 10 percent
Increase 10–25 percent
Increase more than 25 percent

Degree of Change

they plan either to hold their spending on employee involvement activities constant or to increase it. Particularly significant is that only 2 percent of the organizations surveyed plan to decrease their spending, and 64 percent plan to increase it. A comparison between the 1987 and 1990 responses shows a significant difference. The 1987 responses indicated that spending was likely to increase, and our data suggest that it did. The 1990 responses suggest that a significantly larger increase is planned. At least in the short term, employee involvement is in a growth mode. This is consistent with the generally positive picture concerning the fit of employee involvement with the strategic plans of organizations and the results of employee involvement efforts so far.

Table 20.1 takes the issue of future plans one step farther by reporting data on which types of employee involvement activities are likely to see increased use in the next two years. As can be seen, employee participation groups, self-managing work teams, job enrichment, and survey feedback activities are projected for the greatest increases.

Three practices expected to see increased use—survey feedback, job enrichment, and participation groups—already have a very high adoption rate. Their increased use would be particularly impressive because it would mean that they would cover a majority of individuals in the organizations that adopt them. This should create more total employee involvement organizations, in contrast to organizations where involvement is practiced only in parts.

Table 20.1. Percentage Planning Adoption/Discontinuation of Power Practices.

	Completely Discontinue	Decrease Use	Stay the Same	Increase Use	Greatly Increase Use
Survey feedback	1	1	44	47	7
Job enrichment or redesign	1	2	38	57	3
Quality circles	5	11	57	21	6
Employee participation groups other than quality circles	1	0	27	57	15
Union-management QWL committees	5	3	68	22	2
Minienterprise units	6	1	71	21	1
Self-managing work teams	3	0	37	53	7

Self-managing work teams have not been widely adopted, but if the projections shown in Table 20.1 become reality, they will see much wider adoption in the next several years. Of couse, given their already relatively low utilization rate, even with a significant increase they would not necessarily be widely used in organizations. As noted earlier, a comparison between the 1987 and 1990 data shows a dramatic increase in the degree to which organizations utilize such teams. Clearly, self-managing work teams became much more popular from 1987 to 1990, and there is every indication that they will continue to do so. A number of things may account for this trend, including their perceived positive results and the extensive amount of publicity that they have received in national magazines and other publications.

Table 20.2 presents the results for employee involvement–oriented reward systems. Again, some highly utilized reward practices are expected to see greater use. Nonmonetary recognition, as well as work-group and team incentives, are expected to see increased use. Another increasingly popular approach, flexible benefits, is expected to be used more widely by over 50 percent of the organizations. This practice in particular seems to be one that will soon cover a majority of the employees in the Fortune 1000 companies.

Knowledge- or skill-based pay plans are projected for increased use by 50 percent of the companies. This finding fits with the expected increase

Table 20.2. Percentage Planning Adoption/Discontinuation of Reward Practices.

	Completely Discontinue	Decrease Use	Stay the Same	Increase Use	Greatly Increase Use
All-salaried pay systems	1	3	75	20	1
Knowledge-/skill-based pay	2	0	45	49	4
Profit sharing	2	1	71	24	2
Gainsharing	2	0	49	45	3
Individual incentives	2	8	45	42	3
Work-group or team incentives	3	2	30	58	8
Nonmonetary recognition awards for performance	1	1	34	55	9
Employee stock ownership plans	5	1	73	20	2
Flexible, cafeteria-style benefits	1	1	47	44	8

in the utilization of self-managing work teams, since they often go together. Even with this increase, however, they are not likely to cover a high percentage of the total work force.

Gainsharing, too, is projected for increased use by almost 50 percent of the companies. This finding is in line with its support of employee involvement and with the generally favorable results that it produces.

Profit sharing and employee stock ownership plans are not projected for increases by a large number of companies. This may reflect the already high adoption rate of such plans and may also reflect the fact that they are less directly related to employee involvement programs than gainsharing and knowledge- or skill-based pay are. They also do not have the kind of cost advantage that nonmonetary recognition rewards and flexible or cafeteria-style benefit programs do.

The data on future growth of employee involvement programs suggest that organizations are increasingly likely to adopt employee involvement practices in the future. Indeed, the movement toward employee involvement seems to be increasing, and gaining momentum. Particularly significant are that spending is expected to increase and that some of the programs expected to increase the most represent substantial structural changes in organizations. To be more specific, self-managing work teams, job enrichment programs, skill-based pay systems, and gainsharing programs are all expected to show increased use. These programs are particularly important because they, more than most parallel participation programs, directly affect the distribution of power and rewards in an organization. They are also programs that historically have not affected large numbers of employees in organizations. The fact that their popularity is growing suggests that some organizations may be moving toward a time when all or most employees will be in work settings where they have considerable amounts of information, power, knowledge, and rewards.

SECTION 21

Changes and Future Directions

The three years between our original study of employee involvement in America and this one were turbulent for many American organizations. They were marked by heightened competition, organizational restructuring, downsizing, reduction of organizational layers, consolidation, and divestitures. The data in this study present a snapshot, illustrating patterns of employee involvement and total quality activity during that period. These patterns do indeed reflect the economic turbulence of the times.

In 1987, over 80 percent of companies considered themselves to have employee involvement programs. Only a few practices were widely used among companies, however, and for most of those only a minority of employees were covered. Despite limited use of employee involvement practices, companies consistently reported that the specific practices they used, as well as their overall EI efforts had quite favorable effects on performance and on internal operating conditions. Most companies planned to sustain or increase their commitment to employee involvement.

In 1990, there was increased use of certain practices, most notably gainsharing, skill-based pay, participation groups, job enrichment, and self-managing work teams. Although the use of some practices increased, the overall coverage of the work force by employee involvement practices did not change significantly. For the most part, companies continued to be quite positive about the impact of their employee involvement practices, and most again foresaw continued investment in their employee involvement activities.

A number of interesting patterns characterize the use and impact of employee involvement. As of 1990, only a small percentage of Fortune 1000 companies had adopted employee involvement practices extensively. Most others were in relatively early stages of adoption. The gap between the use of these practices in manufacturing and service firms has increased. A striking theme running throughout these data is that companies are adopting high-involvement practices for practical reasons of business performance. Even service firms are more likely than in 1987 to report that they are being motivated by issues of productivity and competitiveness.

This business motivation is evident in the pattern of which firms use employee involvement. Firms facing foreign competition and shorter product cycles outpace the others. They appear to be involving employees to deal with very specific business challenges. Large firms report more extensive application than smaller firms. They especially use practices that have the effect of creating smaller performing units for employees to focus on and feel involved in.

The business performance emphasis is evident also in the impacts of employee involvement. By comparison with 1987, companies are more likely to see increased competitiveness as a result of employee involvement but less likely to report increases in employee satisfaction, trust, and quality of work life. In part, this may be because of the severe methods that companies have had to use to cut costs and remain viable. Business conditions have motivated companies to get their people involved in finding solutions. Such measures as downsizing have also altered, perhaps permanently, the psychological attachment of employees to firms.

The shape of organizations has begun to change. Reductions in layers of management have been the result of general business conditions as well as of employee involvement. Whatever the motivation for such reductions, they have created the conditions, in some firms, for more extensive and profound employee involvement. Many of the practices being used more frequently are those that alter the traditional logic of how firms should be managed. Such practices as self-management, skill-based pay, and gainsharing, for example, move knowledge, information, power, and rewards to the technical core of the organization and base it less on hierarchy.

These changes are reflected in the perceived barriers to and facilitators of employee involvement. In 1990, companies were less likely than in 1987 to report that middle management and supervisory support were facilitators of the adoption of employee involvement. The situation of many managers has changed radically. Numbers and layers of them have been removed. Furthermore, employee involvement requires a fundamental shift in the roles they play. Measured by traditional standards, this role shift can be experienced as a loss of power, status, and rewards.

In 1990, companies were less likely to report that lack of tangible results was a barrier to further adoption of employee involvement. Apparently, they are experiencing the business outcomes they seek. Nevertheless, short-term business pressure remains a major barrier for many firms, as is lack of clear objectives and a long-term strategy. In these difficult economic times, many companies find it difficult to focus on the future, chart a direction, and stay a course for such a large-scale change as the transition to a high-involvement culture.

We examined the relationship between employee involvement and total quality management for the first time in 1990. It was well under way in 1987, and today total quality management is a highly visible part of the landscape of American businesses. Nearly 80 percent of the Fortune 1000 companies have such programs, covering an average of 41 percent of employees. Although total quality management is a more recent phenomenon than employee involvement, the majority of companies see employee involvement as part of the total quality management thrust, rather than the other way around. Total quality may have provided the business focus that was missing in some of the early employee involvement programs.

The good news is that, for the most part, the practices utilized in total quality management and employee involvement appear to be complementary. The use of total quality practices appears to bolster the impact of employee involvement, particularly on business outcomes. This is much more likely if employee involvement and total quality are managed in an integrated way than if they are managed as separate programs.

The findings in this study underscore the systemic nature of the transition to high involvement. Companies tend to be high, average, or low in their transitions overall—they do not tend to focus on knowledge, power, information, or rewards singly. Moving forward in one area requires movement in the others as well. A number of companies have focused primarily on rewards as the lead change lever; these companies have not achieved the highest impact, perhaps because they have not yet brought the other aspects of the organization into alignment.

The practices that have increased the most are those that move rewards and power throughout the organization. Indeed, much more activity is projected in these areas. The patterns of use and change in the areas of knowledge and information sharing are worrisome, however. These may end up being the factors that limit what can be attained through employee involvement. The impact of reward and power-sharing practices depends on an informed and skilled work force. On a larger scale, so does the economic strength of the nation (Reich, 1991).

Our prognosis for the future is cautiously hopeful. In these data, we see signs that companies are aligning their business needs and their management styles. They are integrating the powerful technical tools and continuous improvement philosophy of total quality management with employee involvement. There is a slow but steady growth in practices that reshape the organization to focus more on the performance capabilities of the technical core and less on creating a heavy and burdensome control structure.

The question that remains is whether businesses can make the needed fundamental changes on an organizationwide basis. There is little doubt that changes must be made if organizations are to weather the storms of today and create the conditions needed for long-term viability. There is some evidence that the outline of a new American approach to management is being defined in companies that are high users of employee involvement. This new approach includes the use of employee involvement and total quality management practices, as well as some changes in human resource management practices. It holds the promise of helping firms that adopt it be winners in global markets.

RESOURCE A

The Questionnaire

SURVEY OF CORPORATE
EMPLOYEE INVOLVEMENT EFFORTS

The University of Southern California is conducting a survey of corporate employee involvement efforts. The purpose of this survey is to obtain information on the design, implementation, and operation of employee involvement systems. We define employee involvement as a process that provides employees with the opportunity to make decisions affecting their work and work environment. To further clarify what is meant by the involvement terms used in the questionnaire, a glossary is attached.

The questionnaire is being sent to "*Fortune* 1000" companies and should be answered by the CEO or someone who is familiar with your company's employee involvement efforts. Since this is a corporate wide survey, the respondent may wish to consult key staff familiar with employee involvement systems throughout the corporation. Please answer the questions in terms of *employees in the United States only.*

Your response will be kept *confidential.* The questionnaire is numbered to aid us in our follow up efforts and will not be used to single out you or your company with your response. Your answers will be combined with those of other respondents and presented only in summary form in our report. Your response is voluntary; however, we cannot make a meaningful assessment of employee involvement efforts without your help.

This questionnaire should take about 30 minutes to complete. Most of the questions can be quickly answered by checking boxes. Please return the completed questionnaire in the enclosed postage-paid envelope within *10 days* of receipt. If you have any questions, please call Edward Lawler at (213) 743-8765.

In the event the return envelope is misplaced the address is:

Edward E. Lawler
Center for Effective Organizations
School of Business Administration
3500 South Figueroa Street
Suite 208
Los Angeles, California 90089-1421

If you would like a copy of the results of this study, please indicate your mailing address below.

_____

_____

_____

_____

Thank you in advance for your participation in the study.

BACKGROUND

1. What is the title or position of the individual completing the majority of this questionnaire? *(Check one.)*

   ☐ 1. Chief Executive Officer, Chief Operating Officer, or President

   ☐ 2. Vice President for Human Resources, Industrial Relations, or Personnel (or equivalent title)

   ☐ 3. Vice President for function other than Human Resources, Industrial Relations, or Personnel (or equivalent title)

   ☐ 4. Corporate Manager for Operations (or equivalent title)

   ☐ 5. Director or Manager of Employee Involvement or Quality (or equivalent title)

2. About how many people are currently employed full time in the United States by your corporation? *(Please include any subsidiaries. Enter total.)*

   _____
   (Total number of employees in the U.S.)

3. Of the total number of U.S. employees in your corporation, about what percent fall into each of the following categories? *(Enter percents, which should total 100%.)*

   1. Hourly/clerical   _____%

   2. Technical/professional   _____%

   3. Supervisors/managers   _____%

   4. Other (specify):_____   _____%

                       TOTAL   100%

4. About what percent of your employees work in manufacturing operations?

   _____%

5. About what percent of your corporation's non-managerial employees are represented by labor union(s)? *(Enter percent. If none, enter "0.")*

   _____%
   (Non-managerial employees represented by unions)

```
                          NOTE:
    IF YOU ENTERED "0," WHEREVER UNION AFFILIATION
   APPEARS IN THE QUESTIONNAIRE, CHECK OR ENTER "N/A"
```

2

6. On average, to what extent is your company's business environment characterized by the following conditions:

	Little or No Extent	Some Extent	Moderate Extent	Great Extent	Very Great Extent
	(1)	(2)	(3)	(4)	(5)
1. Subject to heavy foreign competition					
2. Rapidly growing market					
3. Shorter product life cycles					
4. Declining markets					

7. Has your company gone through down-sizing in the last ten years? *(Check one.)*

   ☐ 1. Yes

   ☐ 2. No (If no, please go to Question 9.)

8. If yes, when did the down-sizing occur in relation to your employee involvement effort? *(Check one.)*

   ☐ 1. Before employee involvement started

   ☐ 2. In the early stages of employee involvement

   ☐ 3. After employee involvement was well established

   ☐ 4. Not applicable, our company does not have an Employee Involvement effort

9. Has your company removed layers of management during the last ten years? *(Check one.)*

   ☐ 1. Yes

   ☐ 2. No

3

I.

COMPANY PRACTICES/CULTURE

This section asks questions about your corporation's information sharing, training, personnel policies/practices, and reward systems. (Items with an asterisk are defined in the glossary.)

A. INFORMATION SHARING

1. About how many corporation employees are routinely provided with the following types of information? *(Check one box in each row.)*

TYPES OF INFORMATION	None (0%)	Almost None (1-20%)	Some (21-40%)	About Half (41-60%)	Most (61-80%)	Almost All (81-99%)	All (100%)
	(1)	(2)	(3)	(4)	(5)	(6)	(7)
1. Information about the *company's* overall operating results							
2. Information about their *unit's* operating results							
3. Information about how much fellow employees are paid							
4. Advance information on new technologies that may affect them							
5. Information on business plans/goals							
6. Information on competitors' relative performance.							

4

B. TRAINING

2. About how many corporation employees have received, within the past 3 years, systematic, **formal** training on the following types of skills? *(Check one box in each row.)*

TYPES OF SKILLS	None (0%) (1)	Almost None (1-20%) (2)	Some (21-40%) (3)	About Half (41-60%) (4)	Most (61-80%) (5)	Almost All (81-99%) (6)	All (100%) (7)
1. Group decision making/ problem solving skills							
2. Leadership skills							
3. Skills in understanding the business (accounting, finance, etc.)							
4. Quality/statistical analysis skills							
5. Team building skills							
6. Job skills training							

C. PERSONNEL POLICIES/PRACTICES

3. About how many employees are covered by the following personnel policies/practices? *(Check one box in each row. Items followed by an asterisk are defined in the Glossary.)*

PERSONNEL POLICIES/PRACTICES	None (0%) (1)	Almost None (1-20%) (2)	Some (21-40%) (3)	About Half (41-60%) (4)	Most (61-80%) (5)	Almost All (81-99%) (6)	All (100%) (7)
1. Employment security*							
2. Hiring based partly on employee input*							
3. Flexitime*							
4. Cross-training							
5. Realistic job preview/ portrayal to potential job hires*							
6. Suggestion system*							

5

D. PAY/REWARD SYSTEM

4. About how many corporation employees are *covered* by or are *eligible* for a pay/reward system with each of the following elements? *(Check one box in each row.)*

PAY/REWARD SYSTEM ELEMENTS	None (0%)	Almost None (1-20%)	Some (21-40%)	About Half (41-60%)	Most (61-80%)	Almost All (81-99%)	All (100%)
	(1)	(2)	(3)	(4)	(5)	(6)	(7)
1. All-salaried pay systems*							
2. Knowledge/skill based pay*							
3. Profit sharing*							
4. Gainsharing*							
5. Individual incentives*							
6. Work group or team incentives*							
7. Non-monetary recognition awards for performance*							
8. Employee Stock Ownership Plan*							
9. Flexible, cafeteria-style benefits*							

6

II.

EMPLOYEE INVOLVEMENT INNOVATIONS OR PROGRAMS

This section concerns types of organizational innovations or programs that some corporations have adopted in order to increase employee involvement in decisions affecting their work and work environment. You may want to consider the locations where these innovations/programs exist and then calculate the number of employees involved. Please consult the glossary insert to make sure you understand the terms as we are using them.

1. About how many of your corporation's employees are **currently** involved in each of the following innovations or programs? *(Check one box in each row.)*

INNOVATIONS/PROGRAMS	None (0%)	Almost None (1-20%)	Some (21-40%)	About Half (41-60%)	Most (61-80%)	Almost All (81-99%)	All (100%)
	(1)	(2)	(3)	(4)	(5)	(6)	(7)
1. Survey feedback*							
2. Job enrichment or redesign*							
3. Quality circles*							
4. Employee participation groups other than quality circles*							
5. Union-management quality of work life (QWL) committees*							
6. Mini-enterprise units*							
7. Self-managing work teams*							

NOTE:
IF YOU CHECKED COLUMN 1 FOR EVERY ITEM IN
QUESTION 1, SKIP TO QUESTION 3 (Page 9)

7

2A. About how long has each of the following employee involvement innovations or programs been in use in your corporation? *(Enter number of years in the first column.)*

B. How successful or unsuccessful do you think each of the following employee involvement innovations or programs is in terms of impact on improving your organization's performance? *(Check one box in each row.)*

INNOVATIONS/PROGRAMS	A Years In Use	B Very Unsuccessful (1)	Unsuccessful (2)	Undecided (3)	Successful (4)	Very Successful (5)
1. Survey feedback						
2. Job enrichment or redesign						
3. Quality circles						
4. Employee participation groups other than quality circles						
5. Union-management quality of work life (QWL) committees						
6. Mini-enterprise units						
7. Self-managing work teams						
8. All-salaried pay systems						
9. Knowledge/skill based pay						
10. Profit sharing						
11. Gainsharing						
12. Individual incentives						
13. Work group or team incentives						
14. Non-monetary recognition awards for performance						
15. Employee Stock Ownership Plan						
16. Flexible, cafeteria-style benefits						

8

3. Within the next 2 years, does your corporation plan to **implement, continue to implement** or **completely discontinue**, the innovations/programs listed below? *(Check one box in each row.)*

	Completely Discontinue	Decrease Use	Stay The Same	Increase Use	Greatly Increase Use
	(1)	(2)	(3)	(4)	(5)
1. Survey feedback					
2. Job enrichment or redesign					
3. Quality circles					
4. Employee participation groups other than quality circles					
5. Union-management quality of work life (QWL) committees					
6. Mini-enterprise units					
7. Self-managing work teams					
8. All-salaried pay systems					
9. Knowledge/skill based pay					
10. Profit sharing					
11. Gainsharing					
12. Individual incentives					
13. Work group or team incentives					
14. Non-monetary recognition awards for performance					
15. Employee Stock Ownership Plan					
16. Flexible, cafeteria-style benefits					

9

III.

EMPLOYEE INVOLVEMENT STRATEGIES

This section asks questions about your corporation's employee involvement efforts. By "employee involvement" we do not mean one specific innovation and program. Rather, refer to the full range of innovations and programs that may involve employees in decisions affecting their work and work environment.

A. SPENDING

1. In the next fiscal year, do you estimate that your corporation's spending on employee involvement efforts will increase, decrease, or remain about the same? *(Check one.)*

    ☐ 1. Will discontinue all spending

    ☐ 2. Will decrease more than 25 percent

    ☐ 3. Will decrease 10 to 25 percent

    ☐ 4. Will decrease less than 10 percent

    ☐ 5. Spending will remain about the same

    ☐ 6. Will increase less than 10 percent

    ☐ 7. Will increase 10 to 25 percent

    ☐ 8. Will increase more than 25 percent

    ☐ 9. No basis to judge

B. UNION INVOLVEMENT

2. To what extent, if at all, are unions involved in your company's employee involvement efforts? *(Check one.)*

    ☐ 1. Not applicable - no unions or no employee involvement efforts in unionized operations *(Skip to Question 4.)*

    ☐ 2. Little or no extent

    ☐ 3. Some extent

    ☐ 4. Moderate extent

    ☐ 5. Great extent

    ☐ 6. Very great extent

3. Does your corporation have any contractual agreement(s) with your union(s) covering employee involvement activities? *(Check one.)*

    ☐ 1. Yes

    ☐ 2. No

10

C. STIMULUS FOR EMPLOYEE INVOLVEMENT

4. To what extent, if at all, did the original stimulus for employee involvement efforts in your corporation come from each of the following? *(Check one box in each row. If "N/A," check Column 6.)*

SOURCES OF STIMULUS	Little or No Extent	Some Extent	Moderate Extent	Great Extent	Very Great Extent	N/A or No Basis to Judge
	(1)	(2)	(3)	(4)	(5)	(6)
1. The Chairman or the CEO						
2. Corporate Executive Manager (Vice President level)						
3. Operating Unit Line Managers						
4. Operating Unit Staff Groups						
5. Union(s)						
6. Employees						

5. To what extent, if at all, does each of the following describe the reasons why your company began to implement employee involvement efforts? *(Check one box in each row.)*

REASONS FOR IMPLEMENTATION	Little or No Extent	Some Extent	Moderate Extent	Great Extent	Very Great Extent
	(1)	(2)	(3)	(4)	(5)
1. To improve productivity					
2. To improve quality					
3. To improve employee morale					
4. For ethical/value reasons					
5. To improve employee motivation					
6. To improve employee skills					
7. To make it easier to introduce changes in how things are done					
8. To adapt to future changes in the environment					
9. To strengthen the management of the company					
10. To reduce costs					

11

D. FORMALIZATION OF EMPLOYEE INVOLVEMENT

6. Do your corporation's employee involvement efforts have each of the following design elements, or not? *(Check one box in each row.)*

DESIGN ELEMENTS	Yes (1)	No (2)
1. Formal statement of corporate philosophy or policy on employee involvement		
2. Manual of procedures on employee involvement		
3. Written management objectives concerning employee involvement activities		
4. Separate budget for employee involvement activities		
5. Formal measurement of employee involvement activities		
6. Internal facilitators, trainers, or consulting staff devoted exclusively or primarily to employee involvement activities		
7. External consultants, trainers, or facilitators for employee involvement activities		
8. Assessment of employee involvement implementation in managers' performance reviews		

12

E. BARRIERS/FACILITATORS

Question 7 deals with conditions that are barriers to employee involvement efforts; Question 8 concerns facilitators to employee involvement efforts.

---

7. To what extent, if at all, is each of the following conditions currently a **barrier** to employee involvement efforts in your corporation? *(Check one box in each row.)*

CONDITIONS	Little or No Extent	Some Extent	Moderate Extent	Great Extent	Very Great Extent	N/A or No Basis to Judge
	(1)	(2)	(3)	(4)	(5)	(6)
1. Lack of coordination of employee involvement programs with other programs						
2. Short-term performance pressures						
3. Centralization of decision-making authority						
4. Unclear employee involvement objectives						
5. Lack of long-term strategy						
6. Lack of tangible improvements (e.g., dollar savings)						
7. Turnover in top management						
8. Management culture opposed to employee involvement						
9. Lack of a "champion" for employee involvement						
10. Worsened business conditions						

13

8. To what extent , if at all, is each of the following conditions currently a **facilitator** of employee involvement efforts in your corporation? *(Check one box in each row.)*

CONDITIONS	Little or No Extent	Some Extent	Moderate Extent	Great Extent	Very Great Extent	N/A or No Basis to Judge
	(1)	(2)	(3)	(4)	(5)	(6)
1. Support by top management						
2. Support by middle management						
3. Support by first-line supervisors						
4. Third-party consultation						
5. Availability of resources (money, personnel, etc.) for employee involvement activities						
6. Monetary rewards for employee involvement activity						
7. Decentralization of decision-making authority						
8. Employment security						

14

F. IMPACT

9. How much of a negative or positive impact, if either, have employee involvement efforts had on each of the following performance indicators in your corporation? *(Check one box in each row.)*

PERFORMANCE INDICATORS	Very Negative (1)	Negative (2)	Neither Negative Nor Positive (3)	Positive (4)	Very Positive (5)	No Basis to Judge (6)
1. Productivity						
2. Quality of product or services						
3. Customer service						
4. Worker satisfaction						
5. Turnover						
6. Absenteeism						
7. Competitiveness						
8. Profitability						
9. Employee quality of work life						

15

G. BUSINESS ENVIRONMENT

10. To what extent, if at all, have employee involvement efforts resulted in each of the following internal business conditions? *(Check one box in each row.)*

INTERNAL BUSINESS CONDITIONS	Little or No Extent (1)	Some Extent (2)	Moderate Extent (3)	Great Extent (4)	Very Great Extent (5)	Don't Know (6)
1. Improved implementation of technology						
2. Eliminated layers of management or supervision						
3. Changed management style to one that is more participatory						
4. Improved union-management relations						
5. Moved decision-making authority to lower organizational level						
6. Moved performance-based rewards to lower organizational levels						
7. Broadened skill development at lower organizational levels						
8. Increased information flow throughout the corporation						
9. Increased employee trust in management						
10. Improved management decision making						
11. Improved employee safety/health						
12. Improved organizational processes and procedures						

16

H. INDUSTRY COMPARISON

11. Compared to others in your industry, which of the following best describes when your corporation began its employee involvement efforts? *(Check one. If you have no basis to judge, check item 6.)*

Our company was ...

- ☐ 1. much later than others
- ☐ 2. later than others
- ☐ 3. neither earlier nor later than others
- ☐ 4. earlier than others
- ☐ 5. much earlier than others
- ☐ 6. No basis to judge

12. Over the last five years, has your corporation made a greater, lesser, or about the same level of commitment to employee involvement efforts as others **in your industry** in terms of 1) scope of activities; 2) number of employees involved; and 3) financial resources? *(Check one box in each row. If you have no basis to judge, check column 6.)*

Our corporation's commitment has been ...	Much Less (1)	Some Less (2)	About The Same (3)	Greater (4)	Much Greater (5)	No Basis To Judge (6)
1. in terms of extent or depth of activity						
2. in terms of number of employee involved						
3. in terms of financial resources						

17

QUALITY EFFORTS COMPARED TO EMPLOYEE INVOLVEMENT EFFORTS

1. About what percent of employees in your company are covered by Total Quality Control (TQC), Total Quality Management (TQM), or similar efforts?

    _____%

2. When did quality programs start in relation to Employee Involvement?

    ☐   1.   Employee Involvement started first

    ☐   2.   Both started simultaneously

    ☐   3.   Quality Improvement programs started first

3. How are they managed?

    ☐   1.   Two separate programs

    ☐   2.   Two separate but coordinated programs

    ☐   3.   One integrated program

4. The following practices are often thought to improve quality levels. About how many employees work in units that use the following practices?

	None (0%)	Almost None (1-20%)	Some (21-40%)	About Half (41-60%)	Most (61-80%)	Almost All (81-99%)	All (100%)
	(1)	(2)	(3)	(4)	(5)	(6)	(7)
1. Direct employee exposure to customers							
2. Self-inspection							
3. Work simplification							
4. Cost of quality monitoring							
5. Collaboration with suppliers in quality efforts							
6. Just-in-time deliveries							
7. Work cells or manufacturing cells							

5. Which statement comes closest to describing how the majority of managers in your organization think about quality and Employee Involvement programs?

    ☐   1.   Employee involvement is an important part of our quality program activities.

    ☐   2.   Quality activities are an important part of our employee involvement activities.

18

RESOURCE B

Glossary of Terms

Glossary for
Survey of Corporate
Employee Involvement Efforts

PERSONNEL POLICIES/PRACTICES

1. **Employment security:** Company policy designed to prevent layoffs.

2. **Hiring partly based on employee input:** This involves management consulting with and obtaining employee input about hiring new employees.

3. **Flexitime:** A plan that gives employees some choice in the actual hours worked; for example, telling them they can begin work at any point within a two-hour range. Also called flexible working hours or flextime.

4. **Realistic job preview or portrayal to potential job hires:** Instead of attempting to persuade potential new hires of the desirability of a job, both the undesirable and the desirable parts of the job are stressed in the hiring process. This gives potential new employees a realistic portrayal of the job in order to increase self-selection and prepare new hires for unpleasant conditions.

5. **Suggestion system:** A program that elicits individual employee suggestions on improving work or the work environment.

PAY/REWARD SYSTEMS

1. **All-salaried pay systems:** A system in which all employees are salaried, thus eliminating the distinction between hourly and salaried employees.

2. **Knowledge/skill based pay:** An alternative to traditional job-based pay that sets pay levels based on how many skills employees have or how many jobs they potentially can do, not on the job they are currently holding. Also called pay for skills, pay for knowledge, and competency-based pay.

3. **Profit sharing:** A bonus plan that shares some portion of company profits with employees. It does not include dividend sharing.

4. **Gainsharing:** Gainsharing plans are based on a formula that shares some portion of gains in productivity, quality, cost effectiveness, or other performance indicators. The gains are shared in the form of bonuses with all employees in an organization (such as a plant). It typically includes a system of employee suggestion committees. It differs from profit sharing and an ESOP in that the basis of the formula is some set of local performance measures, not company profits. Examples include the Scanlon Plan, the Improshare Plan, the Rucker Plan, and various custom-designed plans.

5. **Individual incentives:** Bonuses or other financial compensation tied to short-term or long-term individual performance.

6. **Work group or team incentives:** Bonuses or other financial compensation tied to short-term or long-term work group, permanent team, or temporary team performance.

7. **Non-monetary recognition awards for performance:** Any non-monetary reward (including gifts, publicity, dinners, etc.) for individual or group performance.

8. **Employee Stock Ownership Plan:** A credit mechanism that enables employees to buy their employer's stock, thus giving them an ownership stake in the company; the stock is held in trust until employees quit or retire.

9. **Flexible, cafeteria-style benefits:** A plan that gives employees choices in the types and amounts of various fringe benefits they receive.

EMPLOYEE INVOLVMENT INNOVATIONS/PROGRAMS

1. **Survey feedback:** Use of employee attitude survey results, not simply as an employee opinion poll, but rather as part of a larger problem solving process in which survey data are used to encourage, structure, and measure the effectiveness of employee participation.

2. **Job enrichment or redesign:** Design of work that is intended to increase worker performance and job satisfaction by increasing skill variety, autonomy, significance and identity of the task, and performance feedback.

3. **Quality circles:** Structured type of employee participation groups in which groups of volunteers from a particular work area meet regularly to identify and suggest improvements to work-related problems. The goals of QCs are improved quality and productivity, there are no direct rewards for circle activity, group problem solving training is provided, and the groups' only power is to suggest changes to management.

4. **Employee participation groups other than quality circles:** Any employee participation groups, such as task teams or employee work councils, that do not fall within the definitions of either self-managing work teams or quality circles.

5. **Union-management quality of work life (QWL):** Joint union-management committees, usually existing at multiple organizational levels, alongside the established union and management relationships and collective bargaining committees. QWL committees usually are prohibited from directly addressing contractual issues such as pay, and are charged with developing changes that improve both organizational performance and employee quality of work life.

6. **Mini-enterprise units:** Relatively small, self-contained organizational unit (perhaps smaller than the plant level) that produces its own product or service and operates in a decentralized, partly autonomous fashion as a small business.

7. **Self-managing work teams:** Also termed autonomous work groups, semi-autonomous work groups, self-regulating work teams, or simply work teams. The work group (in some cases, acting without a supervisor) is responsible for a whole product or service, and makes decisions about task assignments and work methods. The team may be responsible for its own support services such as maintenance, purchasing, and quality control and may perform certain personnel functions such as hiring and firing team members and determining pay increases.

Construction and Calculation of Index Scores

We presented results on the basis of "index scores" for employee involvement and each element of employee involvement (information, knowledge, rewards, and power). Here, we provide additional information about how the indices were constructed and calculated. Our description is aimed at interested readers who want enough information to understand our procedures, but not at academic colleagues who may be interested in highly technical statistical details about the indices. The latter group of readers may contact us for more information about the measures.

We used standard statistical procedures (factor analysis and internal consistency reliability analysis) to develop appropriate indices. The final indices have acceptable measurement properties and are theoretically sensible. Before final calculation of the index scores, we adjusted the weightings of some variables. These weightings reflect prior theory and research indicating that some practices are more or less important to the effectiveness of employee involvement efforts.

We constructed an *information index* score for each company; this score was the average of the company's scores for all information-sharing practices except one. We omitted sharing information about how much fellow employees are paid because it would have greatly decreased the reliability of the index: the pattern of use of pay information was anomalous by comparison with other information practices. In addition, we assigned information sharing about corporate operating results a weight one-half that of other information practices. We did so because corporate-level information is less useful to employees than other forms of information that they can use directly.

We calculated a *knowledge index* score for each firm; this score averaged the firm's scores for two subscales that we identified through statistical analysis. The first, business-related skills training, included skills in understanding the business, quality/statistical analysis, job skills, and cross-training. (The cross-training variable was included in the survey section on human resource practices; therefore, it is discussed in Section 8, rather than in Section 3.) The second subscale, social skills training, included group decision making/problem solving, leadership, and team-building skills. Each type of skill was weighted equally in calculating the subscales.

We calculated a *rewards index* score for each firm, and this score averaged scores for each of the nine reward systems. The index gave a heavier weighting to skill-based pay, gainsharing, and work-group/team incentives because prior theory and research indicated that these reward practices are especially important to effective employee involvement efforts. Skill-based pay was weighted twice as heavily as unweighted practices, and gainsharing and work-group/team incentives were weighted three times as heavily.

We calculated a *power index* score for each firm; this score averaged the firm's scores for two subscales that we identified through statistical analysis. The first subscale was the average of scores for two high-involvement practices: the use of self-managing teams and the use of minienterprise units. The second subscale was the average of scores for four other power practices: the use of survey feedback, job enrichment, quality circles, and employee participation groups. The high-power subscale was weighted twice as heavily in calculating the power-sharing index because prior theory and research indicated that these practices have greater impact than the others. On the same grounds, the use of survey feedback was weighted half as heavily as the other practices in its subscale. The use of union-management QWL committees was not included in either scale because it did not cluster statistically with other power-sharing practices, primarily because in most firms unions represented either no employees or a low percentage of employees. Since firms that used union-management committees tended to use other power practices to about the same degree, unionized firms were not significantly penalized by our omitting this practice from the index.

We obtained the *employee involvement index* score by averaging the index scores for each of the four constituent elements of employee involvement: information, knowledge, rewards, and power. Each of the four indices was weighted equally.

The final index used in this book is a *total quality management index*. It is the arithmetic mean of the scores for the extent of use of each of the seven TQM practices: direct exposure to customers, self-inspection, work simplification, cost-of-quality monitoring, collaboration with suppliers, just-in-time deliveries, and work cells.

A score on any of these indices may be thought of as representing the degree of employee coverage (measured on a 7-point scale) for the average employee involvement practice included in the index. For example, an information index score of 3 corresponds to the point on the scale indicating that between 21 percent and 40 percent of employees are covered by the average information-sharing practice.

REFERENCES

AFL–CIO. *The Changing Situation of Unions and Their Workers.* Report of the AFL–CIO Committee on the Evolution of Work. Washington, D.C.: AFL–CIO, 1985.

Beer, M., Eisenstat, R. A., and Spector, B. "Why Change Programs Don't Produce Change." *Harvard Business Review,* 1990, *68* (6), 158–166.

Blasi, J. R. *Employee Ownership: Revolution or Ripoff?* Cambridge, Mass.: Ballinger, 1988.

Blinder, A. S. *Paying for Productivity.* Washington, D.C.: Brookings Institution, 1990.

Bloom, D. E., and Trahan, J. T. *Flexible Benefits and Employee Choice.* Elmsford, N.Y.: Pergamon Press, 1986.

Bowen, D. E. "Managing Customers as Human Resources in Service Organizations." *Human Resource Management,* 1986, *25,* 371–384.

Bowen, D. E., and Lawler, E. E., III. "Facing the Customer: Empowerment or Production Line?" *Sloan Management Review,* 1992, *33* (3).

Carlzon, J. *Moments of Truth.* New York: Ballinger, 1987.

Commission on the Skills of the American Workforce. *America's Choice: High Skill or Low Wages?* Rochester, N.Y.: National Center on Education and the Economy, 1990.

Cotton, J. L., and others. "Employee Participation: Diverse Forms and Different Outcomes." *Academy of Management Review,* 1988, *13* (1), 8–22.

Dachler, H. P., and Wilpert, B. "Conceptual Boundaries and Dimensions of Participation in Organizations: A Critical Evalution." *Administrative Science Quarterly*, 1978, *23* (1), 1–40.

Deming, W. E. *Out of the Crisis.* Cambridge, Mass.: MIT Press, 1986.

Dertouzos, M. L., Lester, R. R., and Solow, R. M. *Made in America: Regaining the Production Edge.* Cambridge, Mass.: MIT Press, 1989.

Golembiewski, R. T., and Sun, B. "QWL Improves Worksite Quality: Success Rates in a Large Pool of Studies." *Human Resource Development Quarterly*, 1990, *1* (1), 35–44.

Grayson, C. J., and O'Dell, D. *A Two-Minute Warning.* New York: Free Press, 1988.

Hackman, J. R., and Oldham, G. R. *Work Redesign.* Reading, Mass.: Addison-Wesley, 1980.

Heckscher, C. C. *The New Unionism: Employee Involvement in the Changing Corporation.* New York: Basic Books, 1988.

Heil, W. B. "Reviewing Participation in Decision Making: Toward a Multidimensional Model." Paper presented at the annual convention of the Americal Psychological Association, San Francisco, 1991.

Herick, N. *Joint Management and Employee Participation: Labor and Management at the Crossroads.* San Francisco: Jossey-Bass, 1990.

Herzberg, F. *Work and the Nature of Man.* Cleveland: World, 1966.

Hoerr, J. "What Should Unions Do?" *Harvard Business Review*, 1991, *69* (3), 30–45.

Juran, J. M. *Juran on Leadership for Quality.* New York: Free Press, 1989.

Klein, J. A. "The Human Costs of Manufacturing Reform." *Harvard Business Review*, 1989, *67* (2), 60–66.

Klein, J. A. "A Re-examination of Autonomy in Light of New Manufacturing Practices." *Human Relations*, 1991, *44*, 21–38.

Lawler, E. E., III. *High-Involvement Management: Participative Strategies for Improving Organizational Performance.* San Francisco: Jossey-Bass, 1986.

Lawler, E. E., III. Choosing an involvement strategy. *Academy of Management Executive*, 1988, *2* (3), 22-27.

Lawler, E. E., III. *Strategic Pay: Aligning Organizational Strategies and Pay Systems.* San Francisco: Jossey-Bass, 1990.

Lawler, E. E., III. *The Ultimate Advantage: Creating the High-Involvement Organization.* San Francisco: Jossey-Bass, 1992.

Lawler, E. E., III. Ledford, G. E., Jr., and Mohrman, S. A. *Employee Involvement in America: A Study of Contemporary Practice.* Houston: American Productivity and Quality Center, 1989.

Lawler, E. E., III, and Mohrman, S. A. "Quality Circles After the Fad." *Harvard Business Review*, 1985, *63* (1), 64–71.

Ledford, G. E., Jr. "Three Case Studies on Skill-Based Pay: An Overview." *Compensation and Benefits Review*, 1991, *23* (2), 11–23.

Ledford, G. E., Jr., Lawler, E. E., III , and Mohrman, S. A. "The Quality Circle and Its Variations." In J. P. Campbell and R. J. Campbell (eds.), *Productivity in Organizations: New Perspectives from Industrial and Organizational Psychology.* San Francisco: Jossey-Bass, 1988.

Mills, D. Q. *Rebirth of the Corporation.* New York: Wiley, 1991.

Mohrman, A. M., Jr., and others. *Large-Scale Organizational Change.* San Francisco: Jossey-Bass, 1989.

O'Dell, C. *People, Performance and Pay.* Houston: American Productivity Center, 1987.

Parker, M., and Slaughter, J. *Choosing Sides: Unions and the Team Concept.* Boston: South End Press, 1988.

Porter, M. E. *The Competitive Advantage of Nations.* New York: Free Press, 1990.

Premack, S. C., and Wanous, J. P. "A Meta-analysis of Realistic Job Preview Experiements." *Journal of Applied Psychology,* 1985, *70,* 706–719.

Reich, R. B. *The Work of Nations.* New York: Knopf, 1991.

Rogers, E. M. *Diffusion of Innovations.* (3rd ed.) New York: Free Press, 1983.

Rosen, C., Klein, K. J., and Young, K. M. *Employee Ownership in America.* Lexingon, Mass.: Lexington Books, 1986.

Rosow, J. M., and Zager, R. *Employee Security in a Free Ecomony.* Elmsford, N.Y.: Pergamon Press, 1984.

Sashkin, M. "Participative Management Is an Ethical Imperative." *Organizational Dynamics,* 1984, *12* (4), 5–22.

Schlesinger, L. A., and Heskett, J. L. "The Service-Driven Company," *Harvard Business Review,* 1991, *69* (5), 71–81.

Secretary's Commission on Achieving Necessary Skills. *What Work Requires of Schools.* Washington, D.C.: U.S. Department of Labor, 1991.

Smith, S. "America's Most Admired Corporations." *Fortune,* Jan. 29, 1990, pp. 58–88.

Tansik, D. "Managing Human Resource Issues for High-Contact Service Personnel." In D. E. Bowen, R. B. Chase, T. G. Cummings, and Associates. *Service Management Effectiveness: Balancing Strategy, Organization and Human Resource, Operations, and Marketing.* San Francisco: Jossey-Bass, 1990.

U.S. General Accounting Office. *Productivity-Sharing Programs: Can They Contribute to Productivity Improvement?* Washington, D.C.: U.S. General Accounting Office, 1981.

Weitzman, M. L. *The Share Economy.* Cambridge, Mass.: Harvard University Press, 1984.

Wellins, R. S., Byham, W. C., and Wilson, J. M. *Empowered Teams: Creating Self-Directed Work Groups That Improve Quality, Productivity, and Participation.* San Francisco: Jossey-Bass, 1991.

Wiggenhorn, W. "Motorola U: When Training Becomes an Education." *Harvard Business Review,* 1990, *68* (4), 71–83.